From Arthur's Seat

a collection of short prose and poetry

Volume 7 · 2022

From Arthur's Seat · Volume 7

From Arthur's Seat
University of Edinburgh
School of Literatures, Languages and Cultures
50 George Square
EH8 9LH

Published in 2022

Design and Typesetting by Tim Tim Cheng
Cover Image by Tim Tim Cheng and Eloise Kirn

Typeset in Palatino Linotype

Printed in the UK

ISBN: 978-1-7399635-2-1

ed.ac.uk
fromarthursseat.com

FROM ARTHUR'S SEAT · VOLUME 7

Poetry Editor-in-Chief
Olivia Thomakos

Prose Editor-in-Chief
Vidisha Ghosh

Managing Editor
Medha Singh

Poetry Editor
Shelby Schumacher

Prose Editors
Ai Jiang
Annie Bashaw
Elizabeth DeKok
Erin Ketteridge
Giulia Moriconi
Sarah Newton

Copyediting and Proofreading
Annie Bashaw
Lindsay Oseran
Shelby Schumacher
Madison Sotos
Nathan S. Vived

Art and Design Director
Eloise Kirn

Book Designer
Tim Tim Cheng

Art and Design
Lindsay Oseran

Web Designer
Olivia Thomakos

Director of Marketing
Chandeep Wijetunge

Social Media Manager
Britney Waldrop

Book Launch Manager
Tamanna Dhuppad

Treasurers
Vidisha Ghosh
Olivia Thomakos

Team Advisor
Ryan Van Winkle

Foreword

Dear Reader,

Be aware of what you hold. This anthology is special.

It's like walking into a surprise birthday party where every piece of writing is a hand-crafted gift.

It's like a road trip with your best friend, no destination in mind. You can turn the radio up, roll past town after city. Or you can take your time, pull over, linger where you like.

It's an all you can eat buffet of literature where, yes, you can have seconds at the sundae station.

No, no, it's a luxurious, long taster menu – each foam reduction, each yellow petal and glittered almond curated to dazzle your senses.

It's a thick Sunday newspaper, you can read it in any order you want.

It's your souvenirs. Like your collection of shells, gathered from shores and bars, washed up and dried on your windowsill. It's the sand still in your pockets.

It's voices from 14 different countries. It's 14 postcards.

It's carving your initials in a tree, rock, desk. It's making a mark.

It's a free pass to the fun fair with no height restrictions – spin on the teacups, take in the view from the Ferris wheel, ride the rollercoaster again & again. It's fortune tellers and temporary tattoos. It's carrying home the stuffed purple gorilla.

It's realism, finger paints, impressionism, gothic, magic.

It's a car dealer chucking you the keys saying, 'take it for a spin.'

It's a box of letters from old friends, grandparents, loves.

It's your own mansion with an indoor basketball court, bowling alley, pool and, go ahead, sleep in a different room every night of the year.

It's a fruit bowl ripe with sweet & exotic flavours.

It's like a photo album. It's flicking through your graduation, baby photos, the old bus stop, a shirt you miss, a someone you miss. It's being overwhelmed by it all. It's putting things in frames.

It's a collection of new work from talented authors. It's something to enjoy and hold on to.

Thanks to those who made it. Thanks to you for reading it,

Ryan Van Winkle
Writer-in-Residence

Letter from the Editor

Dear Reader,

It is an honor to have you hold this book in your hands. When I first applied to be the Poetry Editor-in-Chief of this anthology, I had no idea how many hats I would wear (or why anyone would trust me as a treasurer), but as we near publication, I am realizing this challenge is perfect for a poet. We have a joke among our cohort about our Google search histories. People would be quite confused if they took a scroll through, finding for example: "tap dance moves that sound like rain," "mock-up funeral invitation," or some variation of "what rhymes with moan." All this to say we are a curious group with interests that vary. Even if we don't know everything about everything, we will certainly try to convince you that our poetry does.

I cannot adequately express how much I respect and admire the poets who are presented in this anthology. They have challenged me to write differently, to seek opportunities to share my art, and to trust my poetic voice. More than that, I genuinely *like* all of them. How lucky am I to have landed in a cohort of poets that I get to call friends?

I want to thank my cohort for their patience with my

deadline pestering and for sharing their personal work with me over the course of this year. Their poems have made me laugh out loud, ugly cry, and reimagine what poetry can do. I also want to thank our professors, who took the time to give feedback for several of the pieces presented in this collection (and additionally for the cat photos attached to their emails). A massive thank you to Ryan, the Writer-in-Residence without whom this book would be a PDF sent out by Vidisha and myself to our friends and family. And finally, I want to thank you for coming to this page, this book, to get to know the MSc Creative Writing cohort a little better than you did before. With each year that passes, the chaos and crises of our world only make me realize how much we share. Though the writing and backgrounds of our cohort are diverse, I find in so many ways, we are wanting the same things. I hope you find yourself reflected in these pages, perhaps in ways you don't expect to. Perhaps in ways you'll not find anywhere else.

Wishing you every happiness & happy reading,
Olivia Thomakos
Poetry Editor-in-Chief

Letter from the Editor

On 25 February 2022, all thanks to my incredible friend and Poetry Editor-in-Chief, Olivia Thomakos, I attended The Lumineers concert in Glasgow. I carry a distinct memory from that evening. A venue full of strangers, sober, intoxicated, happy, melancholic, determined and lost, singing 'Where we are / I don't know where we are / But it's going to be okay.' It haunted me. Reminded me of all the battles we silently brave. In student accommodations, burning tortillas because you couldn't figure out the stovetop setting. In cafés, struggling to write three thousand words for a workshop, questioning plot, three-act structure, and why isn't this story working? On cold nights with dismal heating, when you feel you aren't doing enough. Yet, we march. We fall through cobblestones, reemerge in the dusty depths of secondhand bookstores and flowers growing alongside Flodden Wall, and all the while, keep writing in the hope that it will be okay. *From Arthur's Seat* is a testament to the writing spirit of our cohort. The soul that wakes up every morning, munches on dry toast, gets a coffee and never stops believing in the eternal power of stories. No two pieces are alike. No two authors are the same. But irrespective of our differences, *From Arthur's Seat* is a reminder of our strength. A reminder of the beauty in our collective and individualistic imaginations.

Our anthology exists because of so many wonderful

minds, and I am grateful to everyone who came on board this journey. To our extraordinary cohort whose kindness and genius made me a stronger, more assured writer. Thank you for trusting Olivia and me with your work. To our professors who have been such inspiring guides and, alongside sharing their amazing feedback, have always made the programme a safe space for our tales of love, heartache, magic, heaven, hell and everything in between. Thank you so much to Ryan, our Writer-in-Residence, for his constant support and beginning every meeting with 'How have you been?' And finally, to our incredible readers for giving us a chance.

I hope you find your favourite story or poem in our anthology, words you can always come home to.

Vidisha Ghosh
Prose Editor-in-Chief

Table of Contents

Poetry

Prose

Content Warnings

Sexual Violence / Assault ∗
Graphic descriptions ☽
Intrusive Thoughts ✚
Gender Dysphoria ⬛
Eating Disorders ϟ
Blood and Gore ⌘
Implied racism ◇
Drowning ≈
Bullying ≡
Violence ø
Murder ✪
Anxiety ∞
Sexism ►
Suicide ‡
Death †
Gore ⌘
Rape ‹

piece has been modified to fit the anthology medium ¤
excerpt from a longer work in progress §

Nicolson Street
by Tim Tim Cheng

Our conversation was cold tangerines
pressed against our cheeks.

Why are you wearing colors, are you
happy? Your response
to a photoed-summer we didn't share.

The green rind, blue stalks
I kept in my wardrobe.

Gusts unpeeled the black layers we wore
as we walked to mine.

I laughed at the top of my lungs
to the woo-ing blows pushing us back,
tin foil snaking into my ears.

I was in my element, the spells of wind
slapping me like happiness. Halfway,

I found that I made us make a turn
opposite my place, and you said,
Here's my bus stop anyway.

We skinned the cold tangerines
to find rejection tinting our fingertips.

ssurances

by Brendon BeMent

Pack up and move on. Go for one last run. Take notice of the palm trees and bougainvillaea—do not forget them. Follow the little dirt paths every which way until your legs ache. Stop. Watch the sunset lather the brown mountains in pink and violet. Go home and say goodbye to the empty rooms, but don't linger. Think about a bunch of grown men roughhousing like children. Realize white walls were a bad choice. Say goodbye to your security deposit. Pack the car and give away a few remaining video games and Blu-Rays to the annoying chubby kid and his friend, always racing around the apartment complex on their scooters. Say goodbye to the dirty street and the homeless and the pulverized pieces of furniture thrown all over the median.

Get on the freeway. Sit in traffic. Continue sitting in traffic. Tell yourself: this is the last time I will have to sit in traffic. Sit in traffic some more. Then sit on a couch, surrounded by your buddies in their new place across town. Drink. Tell them you love them. Listen as they wish you good luck and assure you you'll succeed in all your new endeavors. Say goodbye. Don't cry. Sleep on your friend's couch for your last night, just like the first night you arrived in town. Wake up and beat the early morning traffic out of the city. Give up four years of work, of friendship, of building a home. Drive 2,495 miles back to your parents' house. Reassure yourself you've made the right choice.

You're home. Oh god, you're home. Spend time with your sister: play video games, computer games, watch four-hour YouTube videos on theories about video games. Cook your family dinner. Go for a run, a shorter run. Die on the up and down hills and suck in the thick, wet heat. Sneak out of the house at night. Sit on the driveway and call your ex-girlfriend, who you haven't spoken to since you decided to pack up and leave. Talk over the droning cicadas and see how she's doing.

Don't panic that she might be better off without you. Try not to think about her driving away in the little white Honda going up, up, up the winding driveway and into the trees. Go for a swim in your parent's lake. Float on the water and gaze up at the mountain, now a green one instead of a brown one, and wait until the next move.

Spend the summer mowing grass and cutting circles around the base of trees for eight hours a day. Drive a big truck towing a rickety, screeching trailer and pretend you are blue-collar. Listen to the weird old guy talk about his war stories, buddies dying in front of him, in his arms, on his back—so much death just to cut grass. Ride the lawn mower through city parks and pretend you're on a go-kart. Work on your tan, then apply aloe vera to your sunburns and give up working on your tan.

Drive down the road and spend time with your grandparents. Clean, cook, play cards, go for walks, talk to your grandfather even if he tells you the same three stories all summer. Lie in the same bed you used to lie in when you visited them for Thanksgiving, Christmas, Fourth of July, birthdays, and try to hold on to that fading period of your life. Reassure yourself that none of it matters because the water levels will rise and lead to famine, war, the end of civilization.

Explore your hometown. Walk around the high school where your parents met, go for a run along the river where you flipped over in a canoe when you were five and spent the next ten years being afraid of water. Walk through campus where you did not go to college, but the rest of your family did. Think about calling your ex again, try out those online dating apps instead, immediately feel worse. Eat dinner, watch the six o'clock news with grandma and gramps, go for a bike ride and wait until the next move.

Say goodbye. Cry as your grandmother stands on her front porch waving, your grandfather sitting and smiling next to her even if he doesn't know what's going on, then back out of the driveway and make the return trip down the road. Drive to the airport the next day. Say goodbye again: hug your sister and your mother, shake your dad's hand, watch mom cry, then turn and get on the plane.

Move to another country. Get lonely at night and walk through parks outlined by old stone buildings and cafes. Fall in love with every pretty girl that walks by. Go out drinking and fall in love with every pretty girl in every pub and in every bar. Think about your ex every time you walk home by yourself through the park. Look! There's a castle up there. Stare at the castle.

Reinvent yourself. Study for another career. Go to class and learn how to be a student again. Play volleyball, play basketball, play soccer—football. Try to make new lifelong friends. Have flings that go nowhere. Have flings that go somewhere, then go nowhere a month later. Have a quiet Christmas alone and a snowy weekend in a shack up north with your friends after they've returned to campus. Drink beer, build a fire, share secrets and laughs. Catch a wandering gaze. Don't look away.

Cuddle in the cozy cabin next to the window, wet with condensation from your own body heat and a friend's, who is now more than a friend. Go for drinks, go for dinner, stop going out and stay in together. Spend the last remaining days of the holiday break watching Stanley Kubrick movies. Cook only breakfast food for breakfast, lunch, and dinner. Drink wine and make love all night. Pick up copies of her George Saunders books and read them to her. Lay there with her head on your chest and stare at the ceiling. Take a deep breath. Take your friend who is now more than a friend to the airport and hug her goodbye. Wish her safe travels back home to a place far away, wish her good luck finishing school, wish that she would stay. Swallow the words I love you, because that's silly, and you've only known her for a few months, and you've only been more than friends for a few weeks. Watch her disappear in the security line and go home and reassure yourself you shouldn't have said anything.

Move on. Start thinking about your ex again. Dream of cutting circles around the bases of trees—around and around and around. Invest in a hot water bottle, slippers, electric blankets, and learn to live without heating. Tell yourself if you make it to May, you might actually survive the winter as you walk through the park, along the same path, through the same neighborhood. Stand outside the pub wishing you'd grabbed your scarf when you rushed out to answer your mom's call—her fifth call in a row. Stare at the chapel as she tells you your grandfather has died and imagine his body floating up through the sanctuary of the church and up, up, up into the steeple. Assure your mother that everything will be okay. Wait until your next move. Wait for days as your parents, aunts, uncles decide what to do with his remains, what to do with your grandmother. Try not to think about the vast distances between where you are now and where you used to be. Reassure yourself you've made the right choice coming all this way. Walk through the park and cheer on spring as the bulbs of new leaves hang on the trees like ornaments.

Become a writer for a summer. Climb the hill in town, climb mountains north of the hill in town, swim in lakes at the foot of mountains north of the hill in town. Jump on a train with your sister who's come to visit and spend the hottest part of the summer in Paris, Nice, Zurich, Lake Geneva, the Alps, the Dolomites, the Amalfi Coast, the Aegean Sea, Istanbul, up through the continent and back. Host friends and friends of friends from back home. Take them to all the pubs you've discovered, the coffee shops, the ocean, the hill in town, throughout the countryside. Talk about all the times you used to wrestle and put holes in the walls. Take them to the airport and wish them farewell. Assure them you will see each other again soon. Reassure yourself you'll stay in touch. Try not to think about all the friends in this new place that you did not make—not as many as you'd hoped. Finish being a student. Think that maybe this whole writing thing might work out. Stay awhile longer, linger, but don't decide on how to stay and what to do in order to stay. Reach the holidays and the fast-approaching winter. Pack up your belongings—what you can fit in the singular suitcase you brought, sell the rest or give them to charity shops—say goodbye to your roommates, grab drinks with the few remaining course mates, email professors farewell, go to the airport.

Move back to your country. Move back in with your parents. Call your ex-girlfriend, catch up, agree to meet in the state above you and below her. Spend the night together. Go home and succumb to pressure from Dad. Get a job. Work at the closest supermarket. Try not to think about your friends on the opposite coast and your friends across the Atlantic. Meet up with your ex again. Start calling her every night before bed. Try to write. Try not to think about not writing. Wait until the next move. Visit your grandmother in her now quiet home down the street, have lunch, watch the baseball game, and talk about how they'll win one for gramps. Mow the grass for your dad when spring comes. Reassure yourself you've made the right choice. Try not to think about how you don't have a fucking clue what you're doing. Cut circles around the bases of trees—around and around and around.

Movement
by Medha Singh

Hot tears, hot clouds, hot earth.
Lambent sun, grasping all. Eagles exiting dead trees
beneath sharp rain, they go—as they go: wet, heavy, slow
—perch
on quiet ground, clasping warm
mud in their talons, sienna light lining
their beaks.

When it doesn't rain,
wingèd & bright, they hang
from heaven   stretching out, they
enter that last darkness, they
mirror Vesuvian clouds

        sink—beneath that chorus line of actors,
Ashoka trees in silent anticipation
sink, into a lower earth,
where the sun drowns.

The night, still
as a dark tower.

To Travel Like Snails
by Ai Jiang

They say snails cannot move backward, only forward, circular, or forward in a backwards direction.

To migrate is to move through time, through spaces—both into and out of nations, cultures, and oneself.

1946: SHANGHU, FUJIAN

At the age of six, Daughter sat with her knees drawn to her chest. After hours of tears, all the strength had left her body. Her head rested against the wall in the corner where she huddled. Her expression seemed peaceful, except for the trails of faint white salt dried on her reddened cheeks. Pigtails had once neatly contained her hair—now loose strands stuck out at awkward angles.

She had just enough energy to open her swollen eyes to meet his sympathetic gaze. Anger boiled inside her to see his pity, but she did not show it as he moved to pick her up. Uncle secured Daughter in the crook of his right arm and coaxed her thin arms to wrap around his neck. She reluctantly rested her head on his shoulder and allowed him to remove her from her home. As he walked out, she looked back at the empty kitchen table, which had not seen a meal with her family for a long time, for her family remained bedridden before their passing. She wanted to pry Uncle's hands off and gather as many items as she could hold in her arms, but she knew it would be meaningless.

Uncle shut the front door behind him and Daughter was left with the fading view of the closed entrance—and the neighbouring houses, which had all sat empty for quite some time now. Daughter knew she would never see that door again, and she knew the ghosts of her family would stay there—even though her uncle said they had left—feeling grateful for Daughter's strength. With the thought of her family in mind, Daughter vowed to continue forth, carrying their memories with her. That same day, Uncle became Daughter's Father. Together, they left behind the village that had lost its resistance against the plague.

The mountains were barren of trees but rich with thriving sweet potato crops, whose life masked the death that slept in the graves not too far away. In the mountains stood a small grass hut with a security guard—a designated watch-guard with no real training or credentials—dozing off as he leaned against the hut's outer wall. Daughter imagined that he already knew he could be replaced at any second, but also that nobody would check on him. Every time Daughter passed the guard, she had the urge to chuck sticks at his feet. But on one particular day, she did not feel like doing so.

On that day, she was trudging behind her uncle's family to the flat plain graves near the middle of the mountain. Each of their hands held a small bag of thin yellow sheets marked with red ink.

"What are these for?" asked Uncle's son.

Daughter, who mainly only looked down at her feet during their trek, looked up at her uncle, also eager for the answer.

"It's a gift," said Uncle simply.

"A gift?"

"Yes, so that our family will have great wealth in the afterlife."

Daughter's Aunt held up her bag, which contained dried sweet potato slices. "Not only great wealth, but full stomachs too."

These answers seemed to satisfy the son's curiosity, but only for a moment. "What about clothes? Are they naked?"

A pause, then Aunt shot her son a small, tight warning smile. Usually, cheeky comments meant a smack to the back of the head, but it seemed to Daughter that Aunt was opposed to disciplinary acts on that day.

When they arrived at the clearing, Daughter refused to look at the graves of her family, but she felt the presence of her mother, father, sister, and brother behind her as she stared hard at the clearing in front of the graves. Her unblinking eyes began to dry, then water, until black dots appeared in her line of vision on the sandy ground. She only snapped out of her trance when her Aunt and uncle began to lay the yellow sheets one by one on to the ground in a pile. Their son was about to ask a question, no doubt about why the paper could not be placed all at once, then thought better of it, recalling his mother's earlier generosity towards his insolence that would unlikely be overlooked a second time.

When the pile was large enough, Uncle pulled out a match and set it on fire. As the fire grew, the four began to feed it with what remained of the yellow paper in their bags.

Daughter watched as the growing flame licked each yellow piece that met it, the red ink melting away with the rest of the surface. Some pieces did not get the chance to meet the flame in its dance, but were caught by the gentle hands of the wind and whisked down the mountain and out of sight.

The four watched as the flame grew smaller and smaller until it was reduced to a flat pile of ashes, a thin line of smoke floating from the middle. When the smoke disappeared, they left.

On their way down from the mountain rain began to pour, soaking Daughter, her uncle and Aunt and their son. Daughter's lips lost their rosy colour and her face chilled to white, but she knew this paled compared to what her family had experienced.

1971: SHANGHU, FUJIAN

Daughter became Mother. Her stomach swelled with what she hoped was a second son. Mother's eldest daughter, the First—swaying with her shoulders relaxed—was on her left and the Second—watching for crevices on the packed dirt road—on her right, she walked with unwavering dignity towards the farmhouse at the end of the field.

The Third bumbled behind her two elder sisters until she was able to catch hold of the tail of her mother's shirt, the wobbly walk steadying as she grasped the worn fabric between thin, fragile fingertips. She babbled whatever came to her mind, but none of her siblings—nor her mother—took notice. Soon perspiration dripped down the Third's small face as she had to take two and a half steps for every step her mother took.

The Son trudged against the muddied ground behind everyone else. At only two and a half years old, his feet were already calloused. It seemed like his eyes were constantly wandering, searching for something in the fields, perhaps beyond it.

Together, as they walked down the dirt road, they resembled a line of Chinese crested terns.

"Hurry," Mother commanded, calling to her youngest child in irritated Fujianese.

Son nodded even though his mother could not see. In trying to keep up, he fell often, earning new scratches on his small palms and scabby knees. He neither wept nor complained, ignoring the pain and the dirt that stuck to his wounds and the sweat that stung his cuts like a swarm of bees, his blood and flesh like delicious nectar sitting in wildflowers.

The large wooden door of the house was marked with chips and protruding edges of splintered wood stretched across its impressive height. Only a giant could knock his head against the top of the doorway, which was a great contrast to Mother with her small stature, similar to the rest of the villagers in Shanghu. Mother admired the strength of her fellow villagers. They were built mighty to carry heavy harvests and their energy unending, for work began when the sun rose and ended long after it set.

At the door, the train of daughters broke apart and detached from their mother. The Son kicked off his cloth shoes and ran through the house to the backyard.

The daughters removed their shoes and set them in a neat

row right by the inside of the doorway. The Third picked up her brother's shoes and patted them down before setting them next to hers. Then the daughters dispersed to complete their daily chores. The Eldest collected the dirty clothing of her sisters and brother, leaving them scrambling in only their cloth underwear. The Second pulled out a broom and dustpan.

With a worn wooden bucket in hand, the Third fetched water from their shallow household well—where the water was first collected from the village's communal water pump—and brought it to where her mother rested on a stool near the entrance of the kitchen. The Third set the tub in front of her mother's swollen feet, lifted her right foot over the water, and wiped down the red and purple-veined limb with a rag.

After wiping her mother's feet, the Third dipped them into thecool water, which jostled and spilled over the edges with the added volume. Mother sighed. A breath of relief that escaped her lip only during her pregnancies. It was as though the water had taken away her years of hardship for a brief moment. Mother never talked about her family before the one she had now. When asked about her past, she would laugh and say she could not remember.

"The doctor will be here soon!" the Third shouted repeatedly as she rushed about doing nothing in particular. "He said he'll be here by four!"

Usually, the doctor did not come to the house.

The Son squatted with his white underwear-clad bottom almost sweeping against the cracked stone ground in their small backyard. Overgrown grass and weeds peeked out from between the cracks and tickled the exposed skin of his legs.

With his back turned to the large longan tree, the Son stared intently at the frame of the backyard entrance. The bottom of the frame was obscured by long blades of grass topped off with budding white flowers. From the bottom left to the top where the door ended before the bronzy ridged red bricks of the wall, the frame's peeling green paint was covered by the earthy shells of snails and the translucent residue of slime they trailed—a moving mosaic of earth-coloured rocks, a thin painting that changed its organization every second: a community. At certain times of the day, when the sun shone brightest and the tree beside the well offered no shade to the peeling frame, leaving it bare, with the well enjoying all the shadows. When the tree shaded half of the frame, the snails would gather within the confines of the shadow offered. At night, they crowded the entirety of the entrance's frame, though the Son could not see this—by then it was past his bedtime.

Then, the silence was disrupted when the headless squawking of the Third came echoing throughout the house and the entire neighbourhood: "He's here! He's here!"

The excerpt is a part of a novella—an intergenerational saga on migration.

The Gardens of My Youth

by Shelby Schumacher

Hens and chicks were at my feet
as I strolled through a field of sunflowers,
or *Helianthus annuus*.
I let the sun sweep into my skin
and radiate my smile.
I got lost
in an arch of green beans
and sat on the cool earth to feast
from vine to mouth
until I was collected again.

My next garden was miles away
from the fields of corn and soy
but magical all the same.
There were still hens and chicks:
Sempervivum my mother called them,
and they grew from the black soil
like little green stars. There were fields
not of sunflowers but of dandelions.
With every blossom came a wish
and mine was always to stay.

But I was transplanted to a place
of rolling hills and flat earth
where foreign bodies were treated
like the *Taraxacum* of my former home.
Goldenrod grew in ditches
and the people dubbed it their own,
ignoring the prairie's claim.
Solidago was beautiful though,
living up to the rich name.

After some years festering
in the clay and tall grass,
I found a new home
amongst the sagebrush
and tumbleweeds of a land
that I once believed to be solid pine.
In the sunshine and sandy soil
I sprouted, happy once more
and though there weren't
hens and chicks
or fields of growing sun
I breathed in the metallic desert
and admired the *Artemisia tridentata* in bloom.
There I learned the need for water -
if the parched desert didn't get
its supply each spring
a single match could burn it down.

My final garden was surrounded
by concrete and evergreen
cherry blossom and fern
and there I sat
and grew
and learned.
Some people were like the rain
quenching the desert
or the black earth
fertilizing endless hills of corn.
Still others were nurturing
like the hens to the chicks
and gave knowledge
from which I reaped.
There were also the cruel,
but from each hack

each rip into my roots
I grew stronger
taller
like the sunflowers of my youth.

Home Again
by Olivia Thomakos

When I flew back after ten months,
I made my mom swear
the doorknobs and light switches
weren't two inches lower than before.

The drive into my town never changes
but there is a dollar store where
Kelly Auto always pumped
my bike tires for free.

Elliott is three inches taller
and Luna has a full set of teeth.
The backyard honeysuckle is all torn out,
a stone patio nested in its place. Yet,

the same shoes litter the laundry room,
snack cupboard persistently bare of junk food.
Mom still sneaks off to bed
while Dad stays snoring on the couch.

The Buehler's Grocery sign continues boasting
the best egg salad in the county, and
black coffee remains two dollars
at The Daily Grind where

childhood friends in grown-up clothes
perch to prattle about my *fabulous* time away.
World traveler, bird with no legs, they say
the resemblance is uncanny.

Orange Trees
by Sarah Newton

It was week five of being trapped in my grandmother's house, and Nana was trying to reconvert on her deathbed. One minute she was helping my dad stumble through the morning Shacharit, the next she was attempting to form a cross with her hands, whispering Hail Marys. Covering all her bases, my brother said, just in case the family's last-minute conversion to Judaism four years prior was the wrong choice.

At least, that's what I was told. I hadn't had the time to go and see the spectacle for myself, but my brother Chris always returned from her bedroom filled with laughter and a new ridiculous story.

Mom and I were cleaning nonstop. There was so much to do. Sweep the floor. Mop the bathroom. Put a fresh coat of paint in the rooms. Clean the gutters. The house had to be perfect.

'Alana, you should really go and say your goodbyes. She's been asking for you, you know,' my mother said, sweeping nonexistent dirt out of the kitchen. 'Maybe you could play her something on the piano? She always loved hearing you play.'

'Yeah, maybe. I'll try later, I guess,' I said, running my finger down the edge of the counter to inspect for dust. Nothing ever seemed clean enough. We had buyers lined up, waiting to tour, but it was kind of hard to sell a house that smelled like an almost-dead person.

'She always loved your music.'

As long as it was played through the phone, thousands of miles separating us, so she didn't actually have to see or deal with me after the final note was played.

'I'm serious,' Mom said, tossing a towel over her shoulder. 'You know she only has a couple more days.' They'd been saying that for weeks now, and there she was, down the hall and still kicking.

I nodded again. 'Yeah, all right, I'll bring her her juice.' The oranges were getting moldy in the bowl, and I tried to squeeze as much juice into the cup as I could. It smelled rancid.

But Nana had always loved those orange trees out back. They'd never done anything but produce rotten fruit and take up space, but that didn't stop her from asking for those specific oranges every morning. I was convinced they were actually what was killing her, or at least aiding in the process.

Mom pushed me into the entry hall of Nana's room, a cup of juice clasped between both hands. Pictures lined the walls around me. Portraits of my father and his siblings, with a few candids at the park or in the backyard spaced between them. There was one of me, though I was no more than four at the time. Nana had said I was a beautiful child. Beautiful, but boring. The final number on a wall of grandchildren that she could barely distinguish on a good day.

There was a young woman in a few. Nana. Not my Nana. One that existed in another lifetime. She was always leaning against the orange trees, with its ugly fruits and droopy leaves, even back then.

I moved towards the door, closer than I'd gotten in all fourteen years of my life. Her room had always been some sort of fortress, not meant for the prying eyes or dirty hands of children.

'Go into the light, Mom.' Dad's voice filled my ears, and I crept forward to peek my head inside. He was holding a lamp in one hand, swinging it back and forth like a pendulum. 'Go into the light, Mom. It's time,' he said, laughter seeping into his voice.

Nana just stared back, hands folded on her chest, her face blank. 'Maybe I could get out of this hell if you'd stop blocking me, goddammit it,' she growled. More laughter ensued.

I tried to take a step. To join in on the laughter. Instead, I stepped back out of the doorframe and waited. I waited and waited, hidden from their view, my grip tightening on the glass. The smell of rotten oranges tickled my nose.

My eyes caught on a picture of Nana, young and full of life, as little lines of not-quite-orange juice fell from the corners of her mouth. Her smile mocked me. Reminded me that we were strangers.

I set the glass down on the little wooden stand outside her door, taking a moment to watch little pie es of pulp swirl to the top. What good was saying goodbye to someone you barely knew? Another laugh pierced my ears, and I hurried away, plugging my ears to escape the sound.

*

'Have you said your goodbyes yet?' Chris asked, leaning down to pick up one of the deformed oranges we were collecting. Our every step was accompanied with the soft squish of layers upon layers of decomposing fruit, and the little patches of grass that were still in sight had died long ago, overtaken by citrus.

'Not yet. I've been busy.' There was always stuff to be done. Fruits to pick up. Juice to make. Shelves to dust. Gutters to clear. Furniture to sell. A whole life to pack away, and so little time left to do it.

'Might wanna do that soon, squirt. Mom and Dad keep saying they think it's finally time,' he said, tossing a fruit at me.

Say goodbye. It should have been simple enough; just a couple of words, and it was finally over. The pestering would stop, and the guilt would go away. It was like when your friends left for the night. Just a quick, 'Bye, have a nice time in heaven,' or whatever. Easy.

I walked inside and headed to her room, wiping my hands on my pants. I should turn the air conditioning on. It was getting too hot. It was all wrong. I pulled at my collar. Maybe I could– No. First, I needed to see Nana.

One, two, three, take a breath, take a step. One, two, three, one more step. But I couldn't force myself to take the final step. Why did I even bother? She'd been dying for weeks. She was basically already gone.

I knocked anyway. 'Alana?'

'Yeah,' I said, moving into the room with my hands shoved in my pockets. 'Hey, Nana.'

Some semblance of a smile peeled across her wrinkly face, though not one of her teeth showed. I waited for her to say more, but she only turned her body to the little wooden chair next to the bed where Dad usually sat.

I sat down and stared at her for a long time, waiting for some sense of familiarity to wash over me. I waited for the sadness to seep in. The mourning of someone whose life was no longer happy, like in the pictures.

Finally: 'Do you remember when I was nine, and you threw *my Harry Potter* book into the fireplace because you didn't want me to learn witchcraft?' It was the only thing that came to mind.

She was quiet, her eyes glassy. I tried to continue. 'I remember being so confused. It was just a book, right? And you were finally talking to me, but it wasn't what I thought you'd say, you know? I thought our first real conversation would be so much more than yelling. I wanted it to be perfect. To be perfect for you. I remember being so mad, and Dad just told me not to bring it up again. And that was that. And now we're here. And—' I looked up, trying to make eye contact, but she wasn't looking at me.

Her eyes were cast off towards the window beside me, staring out at those stupid trees, and for just a minute, I could see them like Nana did. Tall and proud, filled with bright orange fruits that children would pick in early spring. Maybe they'd produce millions of fruits. Maybe not. It didn't matter as long as the trees grew. Except they wouldn't grow. They would always be a little too bent and a little too rotten, just like the fruits.

She finally spoke. 'Can you get me some juice?' Then she closed her eyes, leaving me all alone. I nodded. Orange juice. Easy. Something I could actually do.

Grandfather of Mine
by Shelby Schumacher

I live for those phone calls
the ones when before I answer,
my phone flashes a set of smiling eyes
under a shock of white hair,
a photo from that one Christmas
a few years back.

Our conversations are sunshine
and lakeside memories
mixed with weather updates
from his new Arizona home.

His laugh rumbles
talking about the neighbors
and how he's working
like a borrowed mule.
I giggle and remind him he's retired,
he has all the time in the world.

He used to weld with both hands,
and was pretty darn good, I might add.
Ambidextrous like me, or I guess
me like him.

We always talk about the dogs.
My favorite was Gabby
but there was Rubio and Reese, too.
So sweet, the lot of them.
Now he just has Jager,
says it's his last dog
(which he said with the last two.)

I tell him to save it for someone else,
I don't need the reminder.

I've sometimes called
in the middle of the night,
and he always answers.
He sits with me,
drying my tears through the phone.

One day my phone won't ring
and if I call
he won't answer.
I'll curl up for hours
trying to trick myself into thinking
I have one more day
to hear that cigarette-scarred,
Minnesotan farmer ramble.

But his voice will live on
in the messages
I'll refuse to delete.

Hey just checking in,
talk to you later,
bye.

Uncanny

by Giulia Moriconi

There are construction noises coming from the flat above—drill and hammer, drill and hammer, over and over. It's the middle of the night, and Sophie is still awake, tossing and turning in the single bed in her grandparents' guest room. The construction finally compels her to get up, put on trousers and her thickest hoodie over pyjamas. She walks carefully in the dark, dodging furniture and trying not to wake up her grandparents, even though the drilling should have woken them already. The flat feels even odder at night. Ever since she arrived that morning to visit, she has had the feeling that the furniture has been moved, that the ceilings are a different height. The smell is not the same since grandma hasn't been baking as much. More wood than sugar. The books that used to cover the dining table are all neatly stacked on shelves. In the dark, all that's left are the off-kilter spaces that she can no longer move through by memory. Her grandparents swear that the furniture hasn't been moved, that nothing has changed, that she was simply gone for a long time. They have, however, been arguing over whether there's a ghost in the flat. Sophie hopes her light footsteps don't reaffirm her grandma's suspicion of a haunting. She walks out as fast as she can. Halfway down the stairs, she's still wrapping her scarf tight around her neck.

It's been two years since Sophie has been back in Scotland, in the place where she grew up, and Edinburgh's winters are as cold as she remembers. The wind howling almost covers up the construction noises that progressively disappear as she walks down the street. That wind has a way of sinking into her bones, especially now that she's not as used to it. The night is cloudless; no sign of rain. Besides, she won't be outside for long. She's at the bus stop now, leaning on the narrow red seat and taking in the tenement buildings around her. Dark bricks and wallhead chimneys. She's had this tradition in every foreign city she's lived in: she'd get a weekly pass as soon as she arrived, and at least one night, end up riding the bus aimlessly until sunrise. Sometimes it was for gaps in accommodation, which meant public transport was the safest and warmest place to spend the odd night without a place to stay. Other times it was a fast-track way to make a new place feel like home. She's never done that here though, in her own city.

An elderly man with a green bowler hat and a large grocery bag walks up to the bus stop. He places the grocery bag right next to Sophie, and she stands to let him sit, but he stays where he is. The night is quiet. It has begun to drizzle, even though there are still no clouds in the sky, only the almost-full moon peeking through the rooftops.

'Have you seen foxes here at night?' the man asks.

'Are they here usually?' Normally, Sophie would not encourage a conversation with a stranger, but she wants to know the sort of people that live around her family, her would-be neighbours if she were to visit more often or decided to stay longer. She wants to know if there are foxes there at night.

'I met two foxes here once. I was about to get on the bus, but the fox told me to wait here. Telepathically, you see. I got an image— I think that's how they communicate—to wait here because it would come back. Then it ran off and came back with another fox. I saw them here almost every night after that.'

His tone is hopeful and hesitant, as if waiting to be dismissed. Sophie wonders how many times he's told this story and how many people have questioned it. It sounds perfectly rational to her.

'Are you waiting for them tonight?'

The man shakes his head. 'This was a long time ago, when I first moved here. Ten years or so.'

They don't say anything else, just watch the bus arrive. Every sound is distinct. The brakes, the doors opening, the short greetings with the driver, the man's card beeping on the scan.

He sits in the lower deck, among the few who are also out at night, all wrapped in thick coats. Sophie waves goodbye to him before walking upstairs to sit by herself.

The rain turns the view outside into an impressionist painting, with blended edges and the streetlamps' haloes reflecting into each puddle. She leans back into the seat and traces the raindrops on the window as they slide down. Her grandparents had argued about the ghost on and off throughout that day. They hoped she could finally put an end to the discussion, but she hadn't been back in their flat long enough to notice anything unusual that would point to a ghost. It was the mundane details that kept her focus. The fabric and texture of the cushions on the sofa. The washing machine running in the kitchen instead of in a separate room. All things from a past life that she tried to slip back into every time she visited. The ghost was a nice distraction—it gave them something new to talk about. Her grandma explained, as they set the table before dinner, that she would make a point to leave the kitchen door shut every night, and every morning she would find it open. And those footsteps. She promised she could hear footsteps outside their bedroom door. Her grandpa said he never heard them. But he couldn't hear much, supernatural or not. Sophie had startled him earlier that day, when she walked up behind him while he sat on his office chair and tapped lightly on his shoulder to get his attention. It didn't take long to set the table— it was an automatic ritual, one that Sophie hasn't done since she's been living on her own—and by then the conversation had moved on to the food.

As the buildings run past her outside the bus window, there are a lot of unfamiliar store names. She can't see the coffee shop where she used to meet up with friends when she still lived here. In front of her, the monuments on Calton Hill are becoming clear through the mist. Were they always that large, even from afar? She takes her time putting on her wet raincoat and then calls the next stop so she can walk around the city centre. As she steps off, she notices the foxes man has already gotten off the bus. At least she assumes he did; he's not in his seat anymore. She always forgets how much the city smells like bread when the wind is strong.

In the past five years, Sophie hasn't lived in the same place for longer than a year. Four countries and six cities in total. Her grandparents immigrated to Scotland when they were her age; theirs was a one-time move, one that felt necessary. The rest of her family is in England—another one-time move. All day, she could sense the questions her grandparents wanted to ask her, have been wanting to ask her for a long time. Instead, they talked about food, asked if she's eating enough, asked about her odd jobs in each new place with polite curiosity. She wants to know everything about their life, every routine, every odd event. They've been so put together that day, as if a guest was visiting instead of their granddaughter. Her grandparents, who'd worked to rebuild their roots in a foreign country in a time when it wouldn't have been easy and couldn't understand why someone would uproot themselves again and again. She couldn't blame them, even though she wouldn't do anything differently. But now that she's back for a few days, it's easier to first take in the city at night, when everything is different already. Out of time.

There's someone standing in a corner with a full plague doctor costume. The black robe blends with the dark, and Sophie watches for signs of movement to see if it's a person or a statue. The long beaked mask tilts down in greeting as she walks by, and she knows that is a person. She's been walking for a while, and this is the first sign of life she's seen. Somehow that feels normal, just another sighting in the Old Town. She keeps walking. One step after another that sends off a soft echo. She practises walking without making any noise. Further away, someone is calling the same name over and over, but she can't quite understand the name.

She imagines someone calling their dog. Once that stops, there is complete silence.

Sophie and her grandpa used to stand at the window and watch people on the street below. They'd watch for colourful hats, for musical instruments casually lugged around, for animated conversations. It occurred to her, years later, that people must have seen them stare, that they were just as visible. How odd they must have looked, just standing there.

A few hours later, she's on a bus again, heading back. It's getting closer to the morning, although it's still dark out—the sun won't rise for a while. She's dozed off and wakes with the cold window pressed to her cheek. The raindrops are darting down now, too fast to follow. There's laughter coming up the stairs: the type of drunk laughter that interrupts sentences while they overlap each other and don't seem to notice. The couple that's shouting and laughing walks past her to sit at the back, each one holding two cans of beer. After they've sat and the bus stops at a red light, an empty can rolls from the back all the way under Sophie's feet. She decides to go sit downstairs, close to the driver. She's close enough anyway.

She can see the driver's face in the rearview mirror in front of him. The first thing she notices is that his eyes are closed, his lips slightly parted, as if he's asleep. But the bus is still moving perfectly, starts at the green light, turns into narrow streets. The windscreen wipers are going up and down, up and down. The driver is definitely snoring. When she presses the stop button, the bus pulls into the next stop, and the doors open. The driver still does not move.

Sophie doesn't mind walking the rest of the way, even with the rain. She's starting to get used to it. And on the way to the building where her grandparents live, close enough to hear the construction—still going on—there are two foxes. Their reddish fur is the only bright colour in the night.

'I don't have any food for you,' she tells them. 'I'm sorry.'

One of the foxes scurries towards her, then circles around her and keeps running. The other follows soon after, and Sophie watches them disappear behind a corner.

In the flat, the lights are on.

'There you are, little wanderer,' her grandma says.

She's sitting on the sofa and twisting herbs into small wreaths and bundles. Rosemary and lavender. She's wearing her flower-pattern nightgown that she still looks elegant in, even with her grey hair up in curlers. She starts humming to herself as she shifts her attention back to the herbs. She looks so much like herself that Sophie wants to go over and pull her into a hug. Instead, she walks into the kitchen to grab more herbs, then she and her grandma sit next to each other, making bundles to repel the ghost that may or may not even be there.

ᴛe Fo(u)rth Bridge
ᴜჟ Tim Tim Cheng

I came across the bridge you photographed and sent me,
(which you thought looked like the one back home,
five-thousand nine-hundred and eleven miles away).
I almost missed it, dozing off on the bus—but the bridge
to my right was bright like a harp going mental.
Three bridges stand parallel, immense at sea,
each built a century apart: the one to my left
was half-engulfed in the dark, its red oxide tentacles
knotting into fans of steel. I couldn't believe
I was paying attention to bridges, and found them
exciting, looking back to the night when you asked me
to *look at the orange sparks firing off that bridge*
under construction! It was one a.m. The police ignored us
(two adults not street kids, sharing sushi bentos,
a convenience store luxury) by the reclaimed harbour.
I was all eyes on everything, except for your face, except for
those few seconds at your loose brows, highball-blush.
Of all the straight things straight people juggled,
straight talk eluded me: it's easier to say
we can use my face to sell the underwears you wear
than to say *I want to build something with you.*

Room
by Tamara Raidt

In my mind, there's enough room for two.
If you're kind to the butler,

he might let you through to places
I've sealed and locked thoroughly.

But don't you dare go to the attic,
nor even less to the living room:

for wounded memories I tried to save
are rotting in there. Beware!

The ceiling is slowly crumbling,
and I've just painted the wooden floor.

The walls still bear the handprints of old souls
that used to cling to it.

There's a desk with drawers where I tidy
my thoughts for the night,

where a scribe writes down
all the dreams passing through.

Lately I've ripped off the curtains
to let the light reach darker places.

On the threshold, I've thrown suitcases
that weren't even my own.

Yesterday, in my mind, I had an altercation
with the butler who went mad and withdrew.

Yesterday, in my mind,
I made enough room: for you.

Monarch

by Grace McDonald

The city was never quiet. That was why she liked it so much. Even when the time came to take off her headphones and listen to the world around her, she was never met with the deafening silence of her childhood. She supposed that was why she loved him so much at first too. Just like the city, he was confidently loud.

They first met at their local pub—the one with plastic dinosaurs superglued to the ceiling and a bartender that looked like Macklemore. She had been chatting with her friends, nursing her second vodka lemonade, when he walked in. He looked like he had stepped out of a nineties music video with his oversized jean jacket and buzzed hair bleached blonde. She watched as he walked to the bar with his friends, her eyes catching on the freshly rolled cigarette stuck behind his ear.

When he turned around he glanced at her, likely feeling her gaze. Just as he was turning to his friends, though, his head snapped back in her direction. It was a shameless doubletake. They both stared at one another for a moment, and she felt the rest of the world fade as she was held in his trance.

"Ella?" Maeve called.

She shook her head, twisting her torso to face her friend.

Maeve said something, but it went through one ear and out the other. It wasn't long before she felt a tap on her left shoulder. She turned, craning her neck back to look at him. He smelled like tobacco and cloves.

"Can I get you another drink?" he asked, pointing to her empty glass.

"I don't take drinks from strangers," she managed to reply with a coy smile. The alcohol in her system gave her a boost of confidence that she didn't normally have.

"I'm Jules from Glasgow," he said.

"Jules like Juliet?"

"Jules like Julien. You know, like that lemur from the *Madagascar* movie."

She laughed. "Well, Jules from Glasgow. I'll take another vodka lemonade."

He nodded, and went to get her drink. When he returned he struck up a conversation and they ended up talking until last call. As the lights of the pub flickered on he asked if he could have her number.

Ella declared that she would need some sort of symbol of commitment before handing over her personal information like that. He asked for the bobby pin that was failing to hold back a part of her bangs. When she gave it to him he twisted it so that it wrapped around his thumb. He then removed it, pulling on either end of the wire so that the diameter shrunk. By the time he was done molding, it looked like a lopsided anatomical heart. Upon his request she extended her left hand, and he slid it onto her ring finger, promising her that he would replace it one day.

That was five years ago. She was a different person now—the warmth of alcohol and his body from that night a distant memory.

The thin silk of her wedding dress did little to shield her pale skin from the evening windchill up on Calton Hill. She hadn't thought to change clothes or even grab a jacket, her panic blinding her as she ran from the bridal suite.

It wasn't that Ella didn't love him. She did. But not in the way she knew he wanted to be loved.

She had known that truth for quite some time.

She knew when she had agreed to quarantine with him at the beginning of the pandemic. She knew when they adopted a puppy together just after their three-year anniversary. She knew when she turned down that editing job in London to stay with him in Edinburgh. She knew when her father hinted at how Jules had asked for his blessing months in advance. She knew as he slid his mother's engagement ring on her finger, finally replacing that old bobby pin.

For years she had been in such a state of denial that she let him unknowingly dictate every move she ever made. And then, one August afternoon on a walk around the gardens, she saw her.

Ella wasn't sure what exactly made her notice this woman in particular. It wasn't like when she noticed men. With them there was always something specific that caught her attention, like Jules's nose ring and long dark eyelashes the night they met. But with this woman it was simply her.

She reminded Ella of a monarch butterfly with the way she was sitting on the bench, one long leg draped over the other as she stared intently at the book on her lap. Her short auburn hair framed her rounded face, and she mindlessly twirled a strand with her index finger. A pair of gold rimmed glasses sat on the tip of her nose, and she was wearing a black sundress with white Keds.

"They didn't have any chocolate left. So I got mint chip instead," Jules said as he approached with two cups of gelato.

She thanked him, but was still distracted by the woman in front of them. When she took a bite of the gelato, she remembered how much she hated mint chip. It tasted like toothpaste. She wondered what the woman's favorite flavor was.

"When is the tour of the venue again?" he asked.

"Three o'clock," she said.

He started walking down the path, saying something about how he still thought they should have the ceremony somewhere outside.

Ella looked back at the woman, desperately wanting to introduce herself rather than follow her rambling fiancé. Suddenly the diamond on her left hand felt heavy, and she began to walk away. In that moment, though, she was reminded that there was a part of her that she hadn't given a chance. For years she had been so convinced that Jules was the one that she hadn't allowed herself to even consider exploring that other part of herself.

It ate her up inside. But she still didn't tell him. It wasn't until the day of the wedding, minutes before she was expected to walk down the aisle, that she knew she couldn't go through with it.

So, she left his mother's ring on the vanity and ran.

At first she wasn't sure where she was going. Evidently her feet had a mind of their own because they took her clear across town. She didn't care, though. The burning in her lungs distracted her from her bare ring finger.

That's how she ended up sitting atop the National Monument, leaning against one of the blackened pillars as her legs dangled over the side of one of the steps. She had taken off her glittering strappy heels in order to climb up, and they lay abandoned in the dirt below.

Ella wasn't sure how long she had been there when Maeve showed up—long enough for the sun to set. Quietly she watched as Maeve, who she had asked to be her maid of honor only a few months prior, climbed up onto the monument, sat next her, and placed the bobby pin ring in her lap.

"He wanted you to have this," she said.

For the first time since fleeing the venue Ella allowed herself to cry.

A gust of wind struck from behind, blowing her veil so that it hit her in the face. It only made her cry harder.

She wanted it to be him more than anything. What she had to accept, though, was that he was a gale wind, pushing her back to be the girl that he thought she was the night they met. But the woman in the gardens was a monarch, a gentle reminder of the woman Ella had become and the life that she could have if she just took a leap of faith. And, much to her own surprise, Ella was willing to follow that possibility to the ends of the earth.

To Matt
by Han Le

My sadness treads softly
along the memories of us,
the quick kisses of early mornings,
the warm silence that breathed between us.
I'm still here, waiting for you:
        Who never comes.
        Who was lost from the start.
I no longer look for you amongst
the foreign crowds;
But in the surging waves of my sentiments,
the distant, glittering ocean
that resembles your saltwater eyes,
the unreachable sky,
the Tchaikovsky's valses,
all ascent to meet you
who just unloved me.

I still follow my sorrow
to trace your vanishing voice,
which sometimes leads me to that villa
where you almost show up to meet me.
Sometimes, in that bar,
where the mirrors are still dizzy with the reflection of us,
I suddenly confront my startled, solitary figure.
Maybe in that gloomy morning,
the rain showers over this indifferent city
washed away
all the notes of the short waltz
that echo within us.

His Vacant Eyes
by Han Le

My soul is burning like a medieval witch,
as rage fills up all my cells when I see
his vacant eyes. I pause the narration which
I thought would make him laugh, ravel in the glee
of sitting next to me. His absent mind—
unnoticed of my silence for it bathes
in the sea of troubles. His vacant eyes
still look at me—ignorant of the wrath
in my own. His ears only listened to
their master's thoughts. My ego—a little jerk—
refuses to ask for the causes of his blues
but feeds the anger I try to purge.
       Your eyes–still far away. Watching the dawn,
       I question if your love is gone.

Earnestly Yours
by Venezia Castro

A love letter is being read aloud in a public square, next to the cathedral. Sentence by sentence, the reader makes her way through the page until there is nothing left in it but the blank space where the signature should be. She stares at it for a few seconds before looking up.

Above, the sky is empty. It is a bright day but there is no sun. Cold air sinks to the ground and nothing rises to replace it. Her breath becomes thinner. She feels unbearably light. It is winter and the afternoon is white and dry. Weather fit for an execution.

She hears a group of teenagers snickering by the souvenir shopacross the square. They pretend not to look at her but the way they behave is hostile; they point their elbows outward; their voices are too loud. She is sure they have been listening. An old man sits on a bench nearby and stares at her feet. She shifts her weight under his gaze. The pigeons that nested atop the cathedral's buttresses coo and peck the ground around her. In that vacuum of sound, she can hear them clearly. They too are growing impatient.

Soon the Catholics will emerge, freshly doused in holy water and licking crumbs of Christ off their lips. Their pupils, fat after having feasted on the stained glass light for nearly an hour, will be unprepared for the sight of her. She wears no makeup, no bra, no coat and no shoes. Her hair is unwashed. Her legs and armpits are unshaved. Her wrists are tied in ropes she fixed herself. She stands shivering but straight. She will not shrink.

In a way, there is already a noose around her neck. It helps pull her erect; a knot over her throat. She rereads the letter and the lump tightens. She remembers every moment recounted in it and every place described. The writer writes only what the reader already knows.

She doesn't need help remembering. The sweet wine. The rented beds. They held each other's hands as they sat in a public park by the statue of a realist author. He complained about a pain on his side and she cured him by tracing the shape of his ribs with mugwort. He would have died otherwise, but she will never tell him. She did not want that to sway his love or taint the time they had together.

In the mornings, he rested his head against her chest, weakened by the guilt of breaking two hearts as well as his own. In a strange city, visited in secret, she comforted him and listened to him talk about the way he wished things were. He said he wished they could stay there, away, as if they had gone through a door and time didn't exist on the other side.

Now she wishes they had never met. Curse the moons they shared and the blood and rage they pulled and raised.

The first sentence of the letter is an accusation: *You had my life in your hands.*

Who put it there?

Through the thick wooden doors of the cathedral comes the mournful singing. She knows he leads the choir, standing at the altar with his head bowed down to hide his teary face. She knows he enjoys having a stage to show his grief, which is no less real because of this fact. He has been crying every night; she has seen it in dreams without even trying. She is happy that, at least in that sense, he is not coming out of this unscathed.

A life is such a precious thing to leave in the hands of a stranger. How could she have been so stupid?

More people have stopped to stare at the crazy woman whose body will burn tonight.

Nothing is really forcing her to stay but her own will. No one dares touch her. She could vanish, shift her shape and watch the procession from the hill when the night falls, dressed in shadows and feathers, but she is held by the desire to see with her own eyes the hands that penned the letter, the lips that called her whore.

Once, when he could still pretend there was a choice to make, he walked her home in the middle of the night, so late that it was also morning and the streets were empty of cars, and he stopped to kiss her against the ancient wall that remained from when the city was its own kingdom. She loved its agelessness. She felt safe with her back pressed to the stone. She felt like part of something larger than themselves, solid and enduring.

He said he did not believe in destiny until he met her. To this, she said nothing; she just let herself be kissed again.

"To walk alone in the cold at night is such a privilege," she later told him. "I would love you eternally in exchange." When the doors to the cathedral open to let the congregation out, she still loves him. That was her part of the bagain, and she holds her words sacred. But it is love sweetened by decay. She cannot stand the taste of it.

Many of the parishioners pass her without giving her a second look. Their pain is not very deep but it is very ostentatious. Their violent tears make them half-blind, and her dress, though sleeveless, is long and black and plain; it makes her look like one of them at first glance. Others stand nearby, unsure of what to do or where to go next, before their eyes fix on her, who pays attention to no one but to the man who promised her love and therefore freedom, still standing by the casket.

She can make them hear the echoes of the letter, even if they choose not to really listen. They hear her voice without registering at first that her lips are shut tight. Then they realize: she is the offender they all hope to see hang. She is to blame for all that has happened, and to them her hands will be forever stained with blood.

She pushes past those still exiting the service and walks into the cathedral. It is even colder under these high ceilings. She is surrounded by gilded altars. Her bare feet make no sound but candles flicker wildly as she moves past them. He sees her then. Her skin feels like it is burning.

She walks up to the casket and, without addressing the man next to it, she looks in and meets the woman inside for the first time. She is unimpressed. She thought the victim of the story would be beautiful, but finds little to mourn in the corpse of her lover's bride. Her facial features are shapeless; her body oddly proportioned; the poor choice of bright red lipstick makes her look clownish and brings out the shadows in her face, her hooded eyes and saggy cheeks. She was not very pretty, was she? It does not matter, she will not ask aloud.

"I got your letter," she says, putting the folded piece of paper in the corpse's hands. Under the physical ache, she feels mostly disappointment; the pain does not feel worthy. The cast of the drama was underwhelming; the climax pathetic and repetitive. Werther had done the heartsick dying earlier; Abigail pointed spiteful fingers first.

Her bound arms are getting covered in hives.

The man she loves and pities now stands frozen between the pews. He must have caught himself mid-flight. He fears her even now, as her flesh is breaking down, but knows the church and the town and the power of language given to men are on his side. He knows the contents of the letter because he too received one, written by the same hand. He knows he is as guilty as she is, but still would see her hang. How else could things be righted?

She takes a step toward him. She knows he hoped never to look her in the eyes again. He wants her still and is terrified by his desire. He cowers when he thinks she will come closer. She staggers. The smell of charred flesh is stronger than the frankincense. She knows it will not be long before her entire body is caught in flames. The bells of the cathedral chime, untouched, for her; the stained windows swell; holy water turns to mist; the marble pools tremble.

The world is no longer a safe place for her, who is profane and dangerous. He made sure of it when he spread the word about her. "She had our lives in her hands," he said. "She wanted me.

She hated her. She bound my will." He even shed some tears when he spoke of it.

Now he wants this to be over. And it is.

This is the true closure. She will burn, but not as he meant. It will be brighter; a pyre next to the woman who made misery her only trait.

When he thinks of this day, he will think of her. He will remember how, as she burned, he heard her voice reading aloud a letter of love.

I will always thank you for opening my eyes.

She sees herself shining wildly in his pupils.

She will love him forever, as promised, until she is no longer herself.

after the fact
by Amy Curtis

she says she's sorry,
but only when she's caught.
lips that utter apologies
grazed another's; throaty moans
and clenched fists in his hair,
blurring the memory of your name.

she says she's sorry,
but that's barely regret;
she touched your cheek with his
sweat slick on her fingers;
let his love bites bruise;
smelt like his shampoo all summer.

she says she's sorry,
but that might not be enough;
his face now appearing in every picture,
lingering, like her hair in his zipper.
she calls it a mistake, a regret, a fluke,
but her eyes don't look up,

your pincushion heart knows the truth.

Isla
by Eloise Kirn

My skin is silver as a fish, kelp rages in my hair
Anyone who's touched my mane has never left my lair
With my tail I summon floods, with my eyes the storms
Mine is the power of ten horses and the wildness of more
They call me a nymph, a water-horse; a temptress by the name of *Kelpie*
But these are myths made by men, who fear a lass like me
Aye, it's true, I've killed a few – how else would a lass survive?
I swim the streams and ride the green alone on the Isle of Skye
Ye may judge me for my sins, above all what soon I'll do
But don't believe the tales ye hear: this is all that's true

~

I was born from womb to water deep, into the green of an eye
My mother knew Highland pools birth all precious things and aye—
She was a woman of loch and land, my father a man of the sea
We lived in a croft at the water's edge, where grass met pebbly beach
On the glen we had coos, sheep, and a mare named Kally in the barn

59

I had a sister and a brother, both I loved dear, together we tended the farm
But one winter my sister caught a fever and my brother did too in time
Both wept and sweat until they slept, cold in the bed next to mine
My mother birthed another bairn, but the bairn he never cried
In a pool of blood and soft white flesh, both he and my mother died
For a time father and I got by, silent as two herons in the reeds
Wherever he went I followed, like a leaf in his constant breeze
He taught me to fish, forage, and make fire, he taught me to swim and climb
On his bare back and the bow of his boat, he taught me to survive
But then one day he went to sea in wet and winter winds
The waves rose like the wings of birds, his boat soared within
I waited for him in sleight and fright, I waited for seven days
In the tears of a never-ending cloud, I howled like the wind on the bay
At last the sky no longer fell and beams of light broke through
I rode to the cliffs of haloed gold to look across the blue
But the whole horizon lay bare as far as the eye could see
And then I knew besides our stock and mare, the only one left was me

~

When I returned to the croft that eve, a stag stood on the ben

His eyes, wise, locked with mine and headed a warning then

In the silent silver mist he said, *do not carry on*

But young to the ways of the wild, I walked the path beyond

That night three men were in my father's croft, drunk on whisky and rage

They smiled at me through rotten teeth, their beady eyes aglaze

I begged them to leave, kicked and hit, they pinned me down with glee

'Nae wee lass,' the fat one said, 'Now ye belong to me'

I laid there still as a thistle, as they poked me with their vile things

I bled until the men drank so much, all they could do was sleep

When the last eye closed, I rose from bed and took a torch to the fire in the heath

Then I poured their whisky on the beds of straw and lit them up like meat

Past the wooden gate I ran to the barn where Kally stayed

Her eyes wide with light and terror, she threw her hooves and neighed

I put my neck to hers and held onto the black of her mane

Then over the fence we charged as one past the screams and flames

Soon the night consumed us in exile from our home

Save for the calling owls and foxes, again we were alone

We rode the silver backs of mountains along a path of stars

North to the brightest light, north to the farthest shore

On a crescent, moonlit beach, we walked the rocks and waves
Until the ocean swept back exposing a path to the hidden cave
Into an iris of black we went, into a dripping well
The songs of sea spiraled inside like the secret of a coral shell
Here we hid until one morning, when sun rose pale on the bay
I dove for fish out with the great white wings against the gray
Down in the salty hazy green, I felt a lift and a tug
Then the scales of a hundred fish swallowed me from above
A beam cracked, the net came down, I slid onto a boat of men
'Look a lass!' a fisherman said, 'What lass could swim out here?'
'A mermaid, ye reckon?' 'Aye! Must be!'
'I am,' I told them all, 'And if ye trap me, I'll turn the tide, I'll sink yer boat in a storm'
'But ye have no scales, no tail!' they called 'None that ye can see
But let me go and I'll bless yer bay with more fish than ye can eat'
The men looked to each other in fear and wonder
Spelled by both, they threw me over - how easily men believe!

~

Kally and I fled inland at dusk, through thickets dense and dark
In the arms of roots we slept, 'til dawn called the morning lark

My eyes opened to a canopy of illuminated leaves

In the light and green above, wings flit from tree to tree

Then a little bird descended, onto the dew atop the dirt

She bobbed and caught a worm, then she looked at me and chirped

Like the stag she carried a message, this one by beak and wings

Stay in the place of song, she sang, *stay in the place of leaves*

That morning we walked under pine and birch

Across the fertile floor of moss, roots, and earth

The red deer's path led to a sunlit stream

Where on the bank wept a willow tree

I gathered sticks and ferns and here built a home

In the hidden hollow of her dome

Days passed, months passed, in every moment the wild changed

Through the seasons of bloom and berries, I came to learn its ways

In the stream I caught haddock and salmon as they leapt into the air

I fished and foraged with my hands, with arrows I hunted deer

In this time, my shoes shrank, my breasts swelled, my hairy legs grew long

I became stronger, faster, more adept to the woods where I belonged

There was peace in the daily survival, I could've spent forever here

But nothing lasts forever, and death is always near

The day came when everything changed upon the crunch of leaves

Afoot the floor of orange and ochre, a lone man I turned to see

He clutched a stomach soaked with blood, 'Don't run!' he called to me

I ran to Kally as fast as I could, until again I heard his pleas

His body was weak, his breathing deep, he was no older than I

So I made a bargain for his sword, his choice was live or die

In the willow I cleaned his wound, I gave him dandelion to drink

Then I covered him in glittering wood moss and watched him in his sleep

After three days he told me to be his wife, he told me of his home

He said he'd make me a lady, he said I'd be his own

But who could own me? I laughed and spurned his words

'Yer a witch,' he snarled, 'I'll tell the village and ye will burn'

'I'd rather be a witch than a wife,' I said, then I did what I had to do

I held him down and plunged my fists deep into his wound

He shook and bled and then went limp aside the trickling stream

Alone again, I rested, tired and relieved

~

The rowan berries came early, color left the beech and oak

Snow drifted into banks of white, deep woods emptied in cold
When spring came, the birds returned, ice melted into mud
Wildflowers bloomed, loons gave birth, the lochs warmed in sun
One day as I bathed in a falling mountain stream
The sound of laughs and shrieks rolled over the hills of green
I slipped under the water's surface, into the realm of icy clear
But seeing Kally on the bank, five bairns found me here
They begged for my help to cross a rushing tide
With faces like my brother and sister, uneasy I obliged
On Kally's back I carried them, through water over rocks
But the bairns fought as we crossed and a little one fell off
She was swept under the waves, we saw her body no more
Blue she was and full of water once I dragged her to the shore
'Ye did this!' a bairn cried, pointing a finger at me and Kally
He started chanting and his brothers joined: 'Kelpie! Kelpie! Kelpie!'

~

Then the hunt began, amongst dogs and men, with arrows, swords, and stones
Out across every crag and glen, they want me to atone
But I am not a Bogle or beast, I don't have hooves for feet

I cannot breathe underwater, I would never kill a bairn to eat

If they catch me, I'll be killed, if I leap, the same

All I wish is for ye to know: *Isla* was my name

The mob descends upon us, soon truth will be lost to lore

My mare and I ride together now toward the gates of heaven's door

Hair and arrows in the wind, we gallop across the rock in the sky

Into the endless blue beyond, freedom waits on the other side

Free as the birds who fold in flocks

Free as the fox in snow

Free as the leaves that fall like rain

Free as the deer and rose

Free as the berries, braken and brush

Free as the puffin and stoat

Free as the crest of waves below

Free as the leap and the fall –

From womb to water deep

Sweet Milk

by Elizabeth DeKok

I held her after she was born because I didn't want to upset my wife. The doctors had taken the baby away to clean her up, wipe off the blood and goo that covered her tiny body, while my wife recovered in the hospital bed, pale, her skin glistening with sweat. I had grasped her hand and held my head by hers, wiped her brow and fed her ice chips, so I didn't get a good look when the baby came out. I was too focused on my wife, telling her how great she did and covering her forehead with kisses. When they brought the baby back, they laid her on my wife's chest, who held her like she was the most precious jewel, but I looked at her and knew instantly that she was an imposter.

My wife handed the creature over to me, whispered, *This is your daddy*, and I took her in my arms because I couldn't decide right then how to break the news. My wife looked happier than I had ever seen her, her whole face lit up with joy. *Congratulations, you guys*, said the doctor and the nurses, all beaming. The creature felt impossibly small in my hands, and I forced myself to look at her terrible face. One could argue that she had my wife's blue eyes and my upturned nose, and in my exhaustion I probably would have fallen for it, but a kind nurse had brought me a coffee an hour before the birth, keeping my eyes clear. She gurgled and reached for my mouth, and I almost let her touch me, but I handed her back before that could happen. *I think she's hungry*, I said.

The lactation nurse came into the room, started to show my wife how to make the creature latch, and I had to force myself to keep quiet, so I wouldn't yell, *Stop, that milk is for our child*; that thing is stealing it all. But my wife was still weak from birth, so I watched as the creature sucked and sucked and sucked that precious liquid from my wife's breast. When the nurse turned away I swear the imposter looked at me, milk dripping down her cheeks, almost smiling, as if to say, *There's nothing you can do*.

So I sat and watched as the creature drank greedily, and sent texts filled with insincere words to my parents and my in-laws, trying my best to sound ecstatic. We named her Sarah, though I never called her that in my head. I had to keep up this ruse so that I could eventually, hopefully, find out what had happened to my daughter.

*

A few days later, we had to take the creature home, and still I could not figure out how to tell my wife how wrong everything was. My eyes drooped from lack of sleep, but there were more important things to take care of. My wife laid the creature down in the crib for the first time, cooing, her words filled with love, and I tried not to sob as I watched the imposter use our daughter's diapers, our daughter's pink onesies, our daughter's mobile. We had been so excited when we went shopping, looking at twenty different cribs and hundreds of adorable socks and outfits. The mobile slowly spun Winnie the Pooh characters above the creature's head, and she reached up, babbling.

When my wife left the room, the creature looked at me and grinned. Her smile stretched taut over her face until it became almost deformed. I rubbed the sleep from my eyes, and when I looked at her again, she was normal, precious even. I checked her cheeks for any evidence, stretch marks, flabby wrinkles, but her skin was soft and perfect. She felt so delicate under my fingertips. I worried that her skin would rip like paper if I tugged too hard. Her tiny hand grabbed my finger and gave a strong squeeze. She wanted me to know that she had infiltrated the house.

My wife was exhausted, and the creature didn't help, demanding her breast every two hours. We had formula so I could feed her too, but my wife was determined to let the creature suckle until she was too tired to keep her eyes open. I finally insisted that she go to sleep, and that I would feed the creature if she needed more food. My wife collapsed on the bed and passed out instantly.

The creature was asleep in her crib, so I could turn on the computer and let the blue light wash over me. When I was a child, my parents brought my grandmother over from Ireland when she couldn't take care of herself anymore. She had warned me about changelings: *The faeries take the baby and leave a false copy behind*, she said to me as she knitted in her rocking chair. The chair moved back and forth, back and forth, and as a child, I watched her rock for hours, till I would fall asleep. My parents told me just to humor her, an old woman slowly losing her mind to dementia. Even as a child, I had always believed her stories to be silly, mere fairy tales, but the creature made me realize that fairy tales exist for a reason. They're a message, a warning.

I typed "changeling" into the search bar and hit enter, but before I could browse my results, the creature started to cry. I wanted to ignore it, but my wife had only been asleep for an hour, and she didn't deserve to be woken by her tormentor. I closed the computer and picked up the imposter, so light for something that ate and ate and ate. I made her formula while she rested on my shoulder, and eventually she fell back asleep.

*

The weeks passed in such a haze. We both had applied for leave before the birth, so I couldn't even escape the creature by going to work. My wife spent most of the day topless, the shutters drawn so the neighbors wouldn't see. She was too tired to take her shirt on and off in order to feed.

At night, I tried to build a fire in our backyard fire pit, something to bring us warmth and light just for an hour or so, but my wife nixed the idea. The smoke made the creature's eyes water and caused her to wail. Our house had become a black hole, cold and unfeeling, and whatever light I tried to bring into our home the creature sucked up.

My wife's skin turned pale, then gray. The bags under her eyes were almost black. Her nipples cracked and bled, and though I tried to insist on just feeding the creature formula, my wife continued to let that monster gnaw on her. The blood mixed with the milk, and as my wife withered away, the imposter blossomed, pink and fat.

I tried to help. God I tried. When my wife could no longer ignore sleep, I would rock the creature outside while listening to the cries of the woods behind our house. The crickets sang; the owls hooted. Lightning bugs dotted the air like stars. It was during these times when I almost forgot about my child, lost out there somewhere, and almost came to feel something for the creature. She looked like a baby, and I'm only human. Her skin felt soft, and the top of her head smelled like milk sweetened with honey. It was in these moments that I felt like I could accept her, as she was.

Then she would cry for food or to be changed; her shrieks pierced my eardrums like needles. They slapped me back into reality, and I would look into her face and see what she was: a gaping mouth that constantly searched for food, a black hole for a stomach that was never sated, eyes that shimmered with greed. In the forest, almost covered by the songs of the crickets, I could hear the faeries giggle, a chuckle so faint that for a moment I thought it was only my imagination.

*

Sometimes I tried to get the changeling to reveal itself. My grandmother had told me, in one of her more lucid moments, that if you could get the creature to talk like an adult, the changeling would leave, and the faeries would return the original child.

So I tried. When I changed her diaper or warmed up her formula, I talked to her. In full sentences, not the baby talk that my wife insisted on. I went on about my day, about every little thing I was forced to do in order to keep this creature alive. I told her about how many hours I spent washing the clothes she soiled. About how when I heated up her formula, I had to wait and pour a drop on my wrist to make sure she didn't scald her tongue. About how I was woken up every two hours, every night, because I didn't want my wife to be disturbed by the imposter's constant demand for food. It was during these talks that my wife started to give me looks, small ones, that I could only see out of the corner of my eye.

When my wife would go on a short walk, I would try to scare the creature. If you could scare a changeling, it would release your child back to you. I would yell loudly next to her ear, startle her awake. I would drop pans behind her while she was in her highchair, creating a clatter. I thought about pinching her when she wasn't expecting it, but the pinch would have left a bruise on her delicate skin. None of these helped. The creature would only cry, and I would be forced to comfort her, rocking her back and forth so that she would calm down before my wife walked through the door.

*

One day after a rare trip out with her girlfriends, my wife placed a book, *A Father's Guide to Bonding*, gently into my hands. *I think it might help you with Sarah,* I heard her say as I stared at the glossy cover, depicting a man hugging his child, both of them laughing, both of them happy. She picked the creature up and wrapped it around her chest, held snug in the hope that the imposter would feel calm for more than thirty minutes. I could see the bones start to poke out of her skin. Would this monster ever be sated? Or would she spend her whole life attached to my wife's teat, sucking and sucking until there was nothing left of her, just loose skin and a pile of white bones? In my head, I saw the creature crawl over the bones of her mother, completely insatiable, and pick up one so she could suck out the marrow.

I opened the book and began to skim, noting chapter titles such as "When Bonding is Tough" and "Interviews with Overwhelmed Fathers," and that's when I realized that I could never explain to her what was going on. The baby had not only taken her body, it had taken her mind. Any way I could try to explain the danger she was in would be seen as an insane man's paranoia.

My wife had taken the creature for a walk around the block, so I had a limited time to get my bearings before the imposter realized what was going on. I searched the term "changeling" again on the computer, and as I read the results my grandma's stories came back to me, like a whisper in my ear:

The one true way to get rid of a changeling is to burn it in the fire.

*

It was simple, really. When you put the changeling in the fireplace, its true form jumps up to escape the flames, and the faeries return your child. Frankly, it had to be done. She was taunting me, driving me crazy with her laughs and cries for almost five months. I'm sure having to listen to the cries of your own blood must make you want to pull out your hair. Now imagine that it was a monster causing your torment.

There were parts of me that didn't want to do it, you know. There were days when I saw my wife lift the creature up in the air and back down to her chest, over and over, and her eyes were filled to the brim with love. It hurt to know that I would cause her pain, even for a moment, even though I knew that brief grief would lead to a lifetime of true happiness.

I ground the sleeping pills into her decaf tea. Not too much, obviously, just enough to make sure she didn't wake till the morning. It would be the best sleep she ever had, and in the morning her skin would shine with color, the bags under her eyes would be gone, and her breasts would no longer bleed. I would bring sunlight back into our house.

I had to guide my wife to bed, and as she stumbled she muttered, *I want to kiss Sarah goodnight*, but by the time I got her into bed, she had passed out. I tucked her in and gave her a kiss on the forehead.

It was warm and dry out, perfect for finding firewood. Within an hour the blaze was tall and hot, the wood cracking, the flames licking the sky. It was the kind of flame that began to hurt your skin if you got too near. The yard filled with the smell of smoke; it reminded me of roasting marshmallows. I stood and watched the fire, allowing it to warm up my skin, giving me courage. I went to fetch the creature, asleep in her crib. In the moonlight, she almost looked innocent. She almost looked human. I picked her up and held her, in the way that she liked to be held, snug but not too tight, so that she wouldn't cry. She gurgled against my shoulder. I could feel her mouth suck on me, always insatiable. I let my nose almost touch the top of her head and allowed myself a long sniff. The scent of sweet milk was still there, and it caused me to hold her, just for a moment, before I led her into the light.

The Bride
by Lindsay Oseran

John met Lorelei before Lorelei met John.

John had gone out to the beach to take in the sight of the sea serpent, and there it was, rising and falling in perfect arches. The wind was blowing in his ears, and he wondered if the sea serpent made any noise as its mass crashed down onto the waters, or if it slipped into them sounding naught more than a sudden downpour upon the surface.

"Cool," John said, though he was already growing bored, and had run out of saltwater taffy to snack on as he took in the sight. The beach was cold and rank-smelling from the carcasses of crabs strewn about, and the sea serpent wasn't even doing anything that interesting. When John had heard about it, he had been expecting something biblical, maybe even apocalyptic; at the very least, a ship being torn apart.

"It is, isn't it?"

John stifled a squeak of surprise and snapped his head down to see who had spoken, and saw a head with a thicket of brown curls level with his elbow. At first he thought she was a girl, before realizing that her features were too mature to belong to a child.

"You can get the best view of it from our home," the woman said, "but Lorelei doesn't like people hanging around and trampling the grass."

"There's a sea serpent and a mermaid here?"

"Mermaid? Who said anything about a mermaid?"

"From a poem, Lorelei is the—"

"Lorelei is my sister. That's her right there. I'm Miriam."

Miriam pointed closer to the water. A woman was stooped low and pawing through the wet sand with her bare hands, heedless of the way the spume roiled around her ankles and flecked the hem of the dress she wore, a gossamer affair of windblown, white fabric that made John cold looking at it despite his windbreaker.

She was a beautiful image against the bleary setting, like an old photograph superimposed on Friedrich's *Monk by the Sea*. If he squinted his eyes just slightly, her dress blended into the froth and made her look as if she were emerging from it, born from it, an Aphrodite of a colder shore.

"What's she doing?" John asked, if only because she made an odd scene with her dress and the sea serpent in the background.

He imagined that her hands were coated in sand and reeking of the same pervasive brine and seaweed scent as the beach. Her fingers looked long and delicate and he decided that the nails would be plain, trim and neat, except for now when the sand was surely clotting beneath them. Under nail and sand, her skin was probably red and puckered from the water. The image of the red-tipped fingers contrasting with her white skin and dress struck John in his mind's eye and he could not shake it, could hardly give Miriam enough of his focus to follow what she was saying.

"Gathering seashells. She likes to use them in her art. She works with ceramics. Interesting stuff, not the kind of stodgy, old-granny stuff that a lot of the studios around here produce."

Ceramics. It was poetic. Her hands worked the sand now, and later would mold the clay. From the way she scrabbled in the sand, John figured she was probably as hands-on with her art, casting aside tools to fashion raw clay with the visceral intensity of an artist that could not stand any form of separation from her creations.

John realized that Miriam was still speaking and tuned back in, though his eyes remained fixed on Lorelei and the pale gaze of the sea serpent still dancing behind her.

". . . we're going shopping after this, that's why I came in the first place, because Lorelei really can't manage hauling the groceries on her own, but if you're going to be in town for a while you should drop by Lorelei's studio. She doesn't really like visitors, but I'll put in a good word for you."

"I think I will." John tried to keep his voice light, casual, but his heart beat itself against his ribs at the thought of penetrating into the private space of the woman of whom he had become so enamored by sight alone.

"Great, see you there! Just go down the main drag until you reach a fountain with a pizza store to its right, then go past it and another right, and it'll be between the used bookstore and the fish and chips place." Miriam was already running ahead, sneakered feet slipping against the rocks, until she reached the sandy strip where Lorelei was and joined her.

*

"Did you have fun?" Lorelei asked Miriam, letting her pick out a few of the seashells to look them over.

"Mhm." Miriam slipped the seashells she liked into her pockets.

"He looked like a yuppy to me."

"A yuppy? Who even uses that word anymore? I have got to get you out of the house more often. And no, the market and your studio do *not* count. Hey, we should rent a car and take a vacation in Portland!" Miriam hooked her arm into Lorelei's and they started up the beach.

Lorelei gave Miriam an awkward shove that almost knocked the both of them down. "Please, I'd be worried out of my mind about you going home with some strange man. I was just about to call you over from that man as it was."

"Oh, I wasn't looking at him for myself."

"Really? That's not what it looked like."

"Really, I was looking at him for you!"

Lorelei stopped and dug her heels into the sand. "Absolutely not."

Miriam strained to keep walking, then gave it up and released her arm from Lorelei's.

"What's wrong with him? You haven't dated ever—"

"—Dickey—"

"—Dickey doesn't count, you were zoned out of that relationship the entire time and you know it, and anyway, this guy is really handsome. Did you see his hair?"

"Too much pomade."

"Fine, but what about his clothes? They were all brand-name and looked really nice. He could probably take you out on nice dates, and he seemed interested in dropping by the studio when I brought it up."

"You did not." Lorelei's nostrils flared as her hand tightened around the seashell sack.

"I did." Miriam looked infuriatingly proud of herself.

"Miriam!"

"Lorelei!" Miriam mocked back and took off running for the stairs that took one away from the beach.

Lorelei hoisted up her skirts and ran after her. "Get back here so I can kill you!"

*

In a blur of gray days and the sea serpent performing a few more times, a week passed and there was no sign of any man with his black hair slicked back with copious amounts of pomade. Lorelei suspected that she was safe, that Miriam had mistaken the polite gesture of feigned interest with something genuine. It would be typical of her. Lorelei loved Miriam, of course, but she never thought to question what people said or did. Lorelei still wasn't sure if it was a quality that she admired, or if it would be better for Miriam to start probing at the facade to see if it were truly real. She knew all too well that her parents had worried for Miriam after she had been diagnosed as autistic, and that she was expected to become an ersatz guardian to her despite a middling age difference. Then again, her parents had also thought it smart to raise a couple of children on a cliff-edge, so even as a child, Lorelei had put little stock into what they believed.

The bell on the door of the gallery rang out as she scored the clay before her with the needle tool. A customer. Lorelei knew she needed customers to make a living where she could devote time to her craft, but goodness knew she hated them. Most people had no real taste or ability to discern talent, yet they always had opinions. Thankfully Miriam was manning the gallery today, leaving Lorelei blissfully alone to pursue the creative part of her work. Sure, retail was important too, but it was in the same way that cleaning was important to living: a necessity, but absolute drudgery, and all the better if one could foist it off onto somebody else.

"Hey," a voice, not Miriam's, but deeper, a man's, came from the doorway separating the gallery from the studio in the back. Lorelei cursed as the piece of clay she was affixing to the scored spot smushed in her hand, and she turned to glare at the interloper.

It was the man from the beach, tall and lean, with too much pomade in his hair and wearing sunglasses despite being indoors. He was striding into her studio, as if he had any right to be there, eyeing her unfinished and personal projects. It rankled Lorelei to see him looking over the little tiles of glaze and pattern samples lined up on shelves along the wall to the right of the doorway. He made his way past a couple of the tables to stand not far from her.

Lorelei set down the clay and took a hold of the needle tool.

"How did you get in here?"

"Your sister let me in. I didn't really get to see much of your work before Miriam pushed me in here, but it looks nice. I'm John, by the way, it's nice to actually get to talk to you."

"Thanks. What are you doing here?"

"I was wondering if you wanted to get lunch together? I hear the fish and chips place just next door is really good."

"I hate fish and chips."

"Oh, uh–"

"Is that all? This is a business, you can buy something or even commission a piece from me."

"Okay, I see I've caught you at a bad time. Sorry, I'll go," John put his hands up as he backed away.

He caught his hip against one of the worktables, cursed as an unfired statuette wobbled precariously near the edge, and hurried the rest of the way out of the studio. Soon the tinkle of the bell was once more heard.

Lorelei rose and walked over to the doorway.

"Miriam," she called.

"Yeah?"

Miriam skipped over to Lorelei.

"Let's take a break and grab some fish and chips. You and I need to have a talk."

This portion of Bride is an excerpt from the first chapter of a longer novel about a woman who is being pursued by both a man and a sea serpent.

Selection
by Nathan S. Vived

Arthur couldn't sleep.

He lay still on his thin bedroll, staring unseeing up at the pointed canvas top of his tent and listened vaguely to the storm of nasally snores and content grunts of the men dreaming around him; his mind was otherwise preoccupied.

Perhaps, though, it was more accurate to say he was afraid to sleep, to lose himself in the darkness of slumber and entrust his mind to dreams. A dream: the dream that had been haunting his nights for months now and left him filled with dread even in his waking hours.

It was always the same. A sky darkened by slate gray storm clouds, the crack of thunder and flash of lighting splitting the heavens above. He stood alone in the dream, upon a field of knee-high grass that danced frantically in the gale with wind pulling at his hair and wailing in his ear. There were voices in the wind: men shredding their throats with horrified, pained screams; the howling grief of women, high and shrill and horrible; and, worst of all, the cries of babes forcefully taken from their parents' arms, left abandoned and alone to be taken by exposure and creatures too foul to imagine.

He always tried to cover his ears, to drown out the voices, the pain, the sheer and utter grief, but his efforts were always in vain. He couldn't move his body, forced to stand resolute against the storm, and it was all he could do to turn his gaze towards the black horizon and stare down what he knew was coming.

It was always when he did this that the golden light of dawn pierced through the maelstrom, banishing the dark to the furthest reaches of shadows and silencing the screams with a divine choir, beautiful and yet, in its utter perfection, terrible. The choir called to him, sung to the blood in his veins, awakening foreign emotions deep within his chest. Arthur's arm raised unbidden by his own command, the hand outstretched and fingers closing, as if to grasp something that wasn't there but whose presence was undeniable. And there, stretching up into the sky from the horizon, was a rainbow cast from divinity, its colors richer than the finest of silks, than any that could be found in the waking world.

The choir fell silent only to be replaced by a singular voice. It always began as the cry of an infant, high and shrill and innocent, before growing deeper, aging into the spiteful rage of a young woman, morphing again into her wailing sobs. It set Arthur's teeth on edge and pierced his heart like a thousand blades. And it was always that sensation, the impact on his skin and his muscles and organs being split apart, his heart beating itself into ribbons against an unrelenting edge, that woke him in a cold, damp sweat.

Yes, Arthur was afraid to sleep, to feel that pain and fear. He shifted in his bedroll, the thin blanket twisting and tangling around his legs. Cool night air sent gooseflesh up his arms, the little hairs standing on end. He looked out from his tent, past the cloth hem of the partially open flap to the world outside still wrapped in the cover of night.

Even now, he could hear the sounds of the various knights and barons and nobles walking about and drinking around crackling cook fires, their harsh voices muffled by distance. It didn't matter; he knew of what they spoke. It was the same thing everyone was speaking of for the past week, the reason all of them were there.

The sword in the Stone.

A beautifully simple blade plunged into solid rock, its runes proclaiming it Caliburn, the Sword of Selection. The wizard Merlin's prophecy only served to increase the ardor and lust of every man with a drop of noble blood for the sword's kingship. A week had passed with every man of stature in the enormous camp trying to draw steel from stone, and a week had passed with every man of stature failing utterly, left to limp off in shame to lick their wounds. None of them were worthy.

Arthur feared that he was.

Merlin, that damnable old man, had confided in him nearly a year ago that Arthur would prove his mettle to the kings of Britain; spoke prophecy in Arthur's ear of a great kingship, an immortal kingdom, a legacy to surpass the stars, all in his name. A legacy to rival the greatest men of history, one destined to end in tragedy. For what else could Arthur's dream mean but the portents of fate should he draw Caliburn from its imprisonment? A golden age, beautiful and terrible as the dawn, to banish back the storm.

One to inevitably end in death and grief.

Would the golden age be worth it? Arthur could not help but wonder. Life as it currently stood was not so great to not wish for better: nobility ruling with blood and steel over fellow man; beings of fell magic and fae blood controlling the very forces of nature; monsters of man and beast stalking the dark places of the world. A single, unified kingdom could do great good for all of them, bringing unruly nobles to justice, helping regulate the magics of the world, and defending against the monsters that stalked the wilds and shadows.

'But,' a voice in his head whispered. *'But it would all come crashing down like waves upon rock, washing away all the good that you would do, rendering an thing you could achieve as meaningless. Useless. Forgotten.'*

"Is something great because it lasts?" Arthur wondered aloud; his voice quiet so as to not disturb the growing dawn. His stepbrother Kay grunted in his sleep, one large foot kicking out from underneath his thick quilt to strike near Arthur's head. Arthur ignored it, his blue eyes fixed on the crest of the dark hill, where he knew Caliburn waited on the other side. "Am I even the right choice?"

Restless, Arthur kicked his blanket off and left the tent. Maybe the exercise would help clear his head.

Merlin's voice rose unbidden in his mind. *"Tis the Sword of*

Selection, boy. Let the blade decide.'

Could he do it? Leave not only his fate, but the fate of countless others, both alive and yet to be born, to the singular decision of an inanimate blade?

He didn't know.

The twinkling of the stars caught his eye, bright and peaceful and distant. The heavens expanded out before him in all their immense beauty, and he felt a pang in his chest. What was up there amongst the vast expanse? Was it truly a paradise as the Christians claimed? Were Fate and Destiny weaving a great tapestry? He did not know, did not think he ever could know, and yet his mind could not help but wonder.

His feet carried him unknowingly over the crested hill to stand in the shallow valley, the slab of granite holding Caliburn standing almost imperiously in front of him. Arthur stared at it, taking in every detail: the silver of blade etched in ancient runes; the simple but elegant crossguard; the blue leather wrapped around the hilt to form a grip; the polished ball of unknown material that formed the pommel. The Sword of Selection was unadorned, brilliant in its austere simpleness.

It called to him, a siren's song in his mind.

Arthur was afraid to grasp its hilt; he knew it would be warm to his touch.

He was afraid to not grasp it.

The brilliance of the golden sky came back to him, vivid in his mind's eye. Who said it was fate? Merlin, a wizard too concerned with his own perceived genius, and dismissive of anything that did not interest him? His dreams? Why should he listen to either of them? If he claimed Caliburn, he would claim the responsibility that sheathed it, claim the fate that came along with it. He would attain power, power he could use to change the gruesome end in his dreams. He could forge his own path.

Arthur did not know if it would be enough, but, in that

moment, he felt a surge of heat in his chest, and affirmation that he would hold his head high, stare defiantly into the heart of destruction, and carve a new fate for his people. A better fate.

His mind made, Arthur reached with smooth resolution. The tips of his fingers brushed the blue leather, and it was as if the choir from his dream sung in his soul. Warmth shot up his arms as song rang in his ears, and the overwhelming sensation of wholeness settled over him.

Breath held, he pulled.

Caliburn gave.

tunnel

by Liam Wright

you can't see three days ahead

but you can feel

your breath rattling its way

out of unfamiliar lungs

stuck between distorted ribs

crammed into an unknown body

in the shape of a passage

that's only used

to chase the person

you are not now

because you are just a funnel

taking malignant regrets

through this present experiential

collapse to a distant self

that might be you it's hard to tell

when you are just a tube

of rotting meat and gristle

labelled sorted and directed

through this half-life according

to wads of flesh and documents

stuck to you from a time before

you had any choice in the matter

scarf season
by Amy Curtis

hello there, my love, is it time
to pull me out again? the chill
of crisp autumn air shivers
up your spine; your dry hands
rummage through last year's
winter wardrobe, reuniting us.
you recall me feeling softer,
don't you? my colour brighter,
my length longer, less worn:
i have withered in my waiting.

finally, i wrap myself around
your neck, like a lover's arms,
home again. you don't smile
like you used to though, or
snuggle in my warm wool.
do i now itch the soft skin that
you used to beg me to kiss?
i'm sorry i'm no longer new,
but i've dreamed of bathing in
your sweet scent: please don't
discard me, wait, no, not yet!

you cast off my pure affection,
shove me deep into your bag:
i unravel at your rejection, is
the icy air nicer than my touch?
just replace me with another,
cashmere will hug you better.
if i'm lucky, in my next life
i'll reincarnate as your sweater.

The Anti-Seed
by Emily A. Miller

The neighbor's cat is in my garden. This is a problem for three reasons. Firstly, I hate cats. Secondly, the cat likes to shit in the garden. Thirdly, the cat is dead.

It's a mystery to all but God as to how it's died. I push at it with a yardstick, but there's no blood on it, no distinguishing signs of distress. Its body is a stiff mass of fur between my tomato patch and the plywood shelves that hold my planters. My backyard, like my condo, is a matchbox square in a line of identical suburban matchboxes, differentiated only by the festoons of ferns, ivy strands, and flourishing white gardenias. There are no forests around for miles. No predator killed this thing. The dogs around here scream at the sight of their own shadows. Animals defecate when they die, I know that, but for once in my life, this cat is not dropping a deuce in my garden. It's as if God took one of its lives before dropping it back to Earth, but the damn thing didn't land on its feet.

Maybe it ate something. I pull on my gloves and start examining plants for chew marks.

"Chris," I shout.

My husband doesn't even bother to come out. He props the back door open and shouts back, "What?"

"Do you know if anything I grow is, like, toxic?"

"Only after you cook it."

"Shut up. I'm serious. Kevin and Ian's cat, it's—it's dead."

That gets him out of the house. My husband, as pale as I am dark, paces forwards with a crease between his brows.

"Did you kill it?" he asks under his breath.

"Yes, Chris, I killed our gay neighbors' cat," I say with a scowl as I kneel to check my mother-in-law's-tongue. "What's toxic to cats?"

"I don't know, let me—here."

Chris holds up his cellphone.

"Okay, Google. What's toxic to cats?"

"Most household cleaners contain chemicals that are toxic to pets," chimes Google.

"What plants are toxic to cats?" I ask.

"Ah, good point. Here. Hm." Chris kneels down and shows me the phone. "Any of this?"

"Lilies, daffodils, English—oh God, the ivy!"

I stand up so fast that I nearly upend my mother-in-law's-tongue. There's a hanging planter of English ivy on the corner between the yards. Yanking up the elegant tendrils, I examine each. There's not a leaf out of place. Chris is touching the dead cat; I gasp.

"That's disgusting! Wear gloves!"

"Look, if it ate something and died, then whatever it is that it ate is probably still in its mouth, right?" Chris tilts the cat's head back and tries to pry open the jaw. "How long has it been here?"

"I don't know. I came out to check the shoots, and it was just there."

"Have you told them?"

"Kevin and Ian? No." I look towards our side of the fence. "How do you tell somebody this?"

"Ian, your cat shits in my yard, and it leaves stupid pawprints all over my husband's car," says Chris. "So karma removed its soul from its body."

"Chris."

"Okay, fine, I'll call them."

Chris lets go of the cat and goes for his phone again. While he dials our neighbors, I nudge the cat with my foot. It shat in my yard, but it wasn't nasty to me. It didn't hiss, and the few times I'd been to Kevin and Ian's, it had rubbed against me and did that wholemotorboat-purr thing. How could you tell if a cat was old? To me, it looked old. Dark fur, shot through with lighter stripes. Its eyes were closed. What color had they been?

"Hey, Kevin. Um, so, Anaise found your cat in the yard, and it's—it's dead. We thought it ate something out of the garden, but we've looked at all the plants, and there's no sign of anything. Was it—*oh.*"

Chris's voice softens so much on the last syllable that my heart cringes.

"Yeah, I get it. Yeah," says Chris, "I know that can happen. Yeah, sudden. Mm."

"Was it sick?" I ask.

Chris bites his lips together and nods. I can hear Kevin's voice cracking on the other side of the line, though I can't discern what he's saying.

"Is there anything we can do? I mean, it's not much, but we've got—yeah. Oh yeah, if you want to. Oh sure, she's got tools and spades and whatever," Chris says after a moment.

I am being volunteered for something, and judging by the way Chris's voice hikes up, it's not something I'll enjoy.

"What is it?" I ask.

"No, don't worry about it. We'll take care of it." Chris is nodding now. "Yeah, I don't think Ian will want to see. Yeah. Oh, God, that's terrible."

"What am I taking care of?"

"If there's anything else, just ask, okay? Okay." Chris sighs. "I'm really sorry, Kev. No, don't worry about it. It's hard on you guys, we get it. Okay. Take care."

When Chris hangs up, I throw my hands up in the air.

"Mind asking me before you volunteer me for whatever?" I snap.

"I didn't think you'd say no to burying our neighbor's cat," he snaps back.

"Why do I have to bury it?"

"You want them to? You want me to call them back?" Chris brandishes the phone. "You want to tell them, 'Hi, I have a spade and dirt and time, but I really want you to have to bury this beloved cat you've had since you got married eight years ago; yeah, I want you to sob doing that because I just can't be bothered to dig a damn hole.'"

It doesn't sit right with me either, burying a pet, but I'm not about to tell him that. I run my palm over my cheek, thinking.

"I can't bury it in their yard," I say.

"Where do you want to put it?"

"I don't know, just—not there. We could drive out and find a place to bury it," I reason, "but that's still on someone else's property."

"We could throw it in a garbage bag and toss it out with the trash." Chris pulls a face. "They wouldn't know, unless we let the cat out of the bag."

"Why would we—God, Chris, you're horrible." Despite myself, I laugh.

Chris chuckles too, but the question is still lying there like the furry corpse on the grass.

"I don't think I'm okay with just throwing it out. We need to bury it. It's an animal, it ought to go back to the earth," I hear myself say.

"Okay, where?"

I run my nails along my face. The summer heat has me sweating, but my hands are strangely cold.

"Right here," I say, "where it died."

"In our yard? You want to bury a cat in our yard?"

"Where else is it going to go? We'll wrap it in newspaper, I'll dig the hole, and we'll bury it. I meant to plant something there anyway," I lie.

Chris has one hand in his straw-blonde hair and the other on his hip. He stares at the dead cat for a long moment, then exhales.

"It's your garden. What do you want me to do?" he asks.

I love him for that—that *let's-get-it-done* attitude. He makes short work of the corpse, wrapping it in The Public Times and binding it with twine from the kitchen. I take my spade and break the turf right where the cat died. Under the green is a few inches of hard, intertwined roots. Below that is soft dirt that quickly gives out to hard clay. Digging a hole deep enough to bury the cat is not easy. I end up with dirt smeared up to my shoulder and grass stains on my sleeve. Worms, ants, and beetles all come thralling out of the walls of the hole. I barely pay attention. Breaking the earth has all my focus.

"Deep enough?" I ask with a pant.

"Deep enough." Chris has the newspaper bundle under one arm. "Watch out."

"Don't just drop it in!"

"Fine, fine."

He kneels, then lowers the bundle until it hits the bottom. As we pile dirt over top of it, the newspaper gives way a bit, and the cat is compressed into the earth. I toss the turf in upside-down before piling the rest of the dirt on top of it.

"What are you going to plant here," Chris asks.

"I don't know yet. Something," I say quickly, "but I don't know yet."

*

The patch of bare dirt in the backyard grows on me. For the next few weeks, when I go out to the garden, I consider that patch of dirt. Something that was alive is now dead, and I've put it under the dirt. One night, as we're lying in bed, I tell Chris that I keep thinking about it as an anti-seed.

"Anti-seed," he repeats.

"A seed isn't really alive until it starts growing. You plant it," I explain, "and it becomes a living thing. What we did was plant something that was dead."

"Anaise, you're creeping me out."

"Sorry. I just can't stop thinking about it."

"Plant something there," he urges me, "or I will grab

something and shove it in that dirt."

I am not much of a herb gardener, but I end up planting catmint. It feels right, somehow, and the irony isn't lost on me. We don't tell Ian and Kevin where their cat is. Burying it so close to their home, yet not in their home, feels almost like trespassing.

They never ask, so it makes it easy to hide. The catmint blossoms the next year; at the same time, Ian and Kevin get a new cat.

It's scarcely bigger than a kitten, this marmalade. When I step outside and see it chewing on the catmint, I laugh until I cry. Ian hears me, sees what's going on, and practically leaps over the fence to grab her. He apologizes; he knows how I feel about my plants. My face hurts from grinning, and there are tear tracks on my face, but when I try to explain, I can't.

I clip off a few sprigs for him to take back, and Ian takes his cat home.

Caliban's Revenge
by Christopher Corbett

The buck, his neck taut, was protected by a wall of trees. His long outline and the impressive tangle of antlers were discernible here and there amid the interlacing branches. He turned his head sharply to the left, perturbed, and plodded forward, patches of his warm, chestnut fur poking out between the scraggly trees. His head bobbed gently, like a toddler nodding off, until he stopped and listened, but he heard nothing save the soft rustle of leaves and the lilt of the breeze flowing through the trees. The deer pressed on, his head held low, measuring each step. The crosshairs matched his gait. He vanished down a ravine, and the crosshairs scanned the horizon conscientiously for his potential return. The sun was beginning to set, and visibility would soon be gone.

The sharp ends and delicate loops of his antlers crept in sudden jerks from beneath a mound of dry earth. He broke into a light trot, racing from the dark, intersecting lines that tried to split his neck down the middle, but they followed clumsily after him. It was only when the buck burst into the clearing–his long, thin legs swinging like pendulums, his head tossing boisterously–that the crosshairs could appreciate the full majesty of the beast. The antlers sprang from his crown like the wings of an eagle. He bounded across the plane, the folds of his muscles cranking and churning like the pistons in a locomotive, trampling the short grass under his dainty hooves. He stopped in the centre of the clearing, awash in a sea of plush grass, and skittishly lowered his head to the ground and chomped ravenously. A harsh breeze hurtled across the plane, the spindly grass bowing with its passage and the short, spotted fur of the buck twitched. The thin, black lines painted on his long, elegant neck jerked furiously, and when they came back down, they saw the deer bounce, like his legs were springs, and dart away, bounding in a circle, his head swinging from side to side. A little laugh came from behind the crosshairs.

Before the buck heard the crack of the rifle scream in his ears, he felt it whip at his bone and cleave his flesh. He felt like a balloon about to pop. He beat his legs and pulled up clods of earth and clumps of grass with his violent pounding. His body strived for life, but his mind had yet to click, so his legs were pumping, and his heart was pounding, pouring blood from him, but he was going in circles. He was expecting it again, another one, whatever it was, to smart him. His mind came back into focus, and he saw the line of trees in the distance. The air felt thick, like he was wading through mud, but the dry ground met his stampeding hooves like a kiss. It was impossible to tell when it would come again. He was almost at the tree line, could almost feel the bristle of the leaves on his fur, when his back leg, left leg, started dragging. Maybe he could still get something out of it; yes, yes, but no, nothing, it was deflating, useless. Another shot rang out.

He heard it but never felt it. He broke through the treeline and slowed to a gentle trot so his antlers wouldn't get caught anywhere, thin branches brushing him and their little leaves stroking his fur. His leg was searing hot, as if the hard ground grabbed hold of it with each step he took and tried to wrench it from his body. He wanted to lie down, curl into a tight ball in the rays of a warm sun and have some great deer dote on him, her head softly nuzzling his, her warm tongue lapping at his cold gnarled face. But he hobbled on, his leg going stiff like it was shrinking and shrivelling. It was starting to get dark. He walked now, his hind leg buckling under the pressure, trying to hold his head a little higher than the droop it was falling to.

The sun set, and darkness fell on the forest. The shade of the tall trees and thorny bushes lurched across the hard ground until it disappeared into the soil. An owl hooted gently, and in the wake of the long, round note, the forest fell silent before it bubbled again with the weak murmur of animals and insects innumerable and the faint croon of wind blowing ceaselessly. The first drop of rain patted a dry mound of dirt in a circle of tall trees. It was followed closely by another faint drop, and more plopped—on the coarse mound, the dry bark of the tall trees, the brittle branches half crumpled and snapped scattered around the earth now wet with spittle, now moist and softening, now sludge, awash with the pouring rain. The cacophony grew, like the wail of a babe, in fits and starts, until the notes rose full pitch and the ostensible momentary silence bellowed the notes ever louder.

The buck was fast asleep in a warm coppice. The tough, prickly leaves shielded him from the worst of the rain, so only a few drops patted his face. They fell weakly on his slack stomach bulging out with each heave; and on the shins of his long, thin legs curled in tight; and on the mass of antlers sprouting from his crown. The rain fell on his leg, the bloody hole open to the sky, and streamed in red, meagre lines down his hind.

The buck, then a fawn, came sliding out his mother, slick, coming to a rest on the fleecy grass. He opened his eyes, and when he could finally see without the brightness blinding him, he watched the blue sky creep through the sharp blades of grass poking out from around his snout nestled in the ground. There was a tongue on him. He looked up and saw the shadow of a long neck blocking out the sun, and felt the coarse grain scrape against him and the weak trickle of spittle drip down the side of his back and flow round his little stomach and soak into the soft earth. She pulled back, and he saw the long arc she made as she wound her head back down to earth. He tried his legs and found, with a little effort, he could get up a bit on them. And from his knees he could get all the way up. He went over to his panting mother and inspected her with his nose. He saw from the corner of his eye there was another thing coming out, and he watched, mystified, at its slow crawl into life. She reached over again and licked this one clean. And when he got to his feet, this other deer, he did it quickly and shot off away from their mother without even giving her enough time to finish her licking.

He nestled on the grass by his mother and went to sucking

on the bulbous nibs poking from her stomach. The sweet milk, from the first drop, was magnificent, so pure. But she jerked, his mother, and her whole body lept in the air, her legs bucking out behind her, and she let out a terrible wail. Confused, but hungry, the little fawn went for the nib again when she landed, but she jumped to her feet and backed away, her eyes flailing. He didn't know what was wrong, whether there was something else stuck inside her, perhaps another sibling, but he approached cautiously. She backed away and spun wildly with big steps, turning and turning. The other fawn galloped back to them silly with excitement. He stopped skittishly, and they watched their mother cry to the forest, the echo still singing as she fell to the ground with a thud, and the deep, aching breathes she took, her gaping mouth lodged in the ground, tongue splayed over her teeth. She was dead when another doe found them curled under the crook of her leg a few days later.

The buck woke with the sun shining through the branches above him. He twisted around and inspected his wound, sniffing, and lapped tentatively at it with his long tongue. He poked his head up, and, finding nothing to hold his attention, lazily set it back down against a mass of leaves.

He rested for a few days, venturing out as little as possible. Eventually, he decided he'd like a walk, and when the sun woke him, he rose and stepped out of the thicket with a slight limp.

*

His brother died years ago, not long after their mother. He was always wandering off, his brother. Their new doe mother would turn her head incredulously when he was nowhere to be found, and wore a vacant, wandering look in her eyes as she watched the tree line on the edge of the herd as darkness crept in. One day he didn't come home. He went out, the little buck, scooting passed his mother lying desultory on the damp grass. He galloped frantically between the trees, loose leaves hanging from the long branches of sycamore and the tiny spikes of tall coniferous trees staring at him. The mud sucked his hooves in deeper with each vigorous step, dragging him to a halt against his wild and quickening pace. He found a stain of blood splattered across a clearing beside chomped grass. He crawled to a standstill above the scene and eased his body down like he was stepping into cold water. His brother's smell did not fit with the wet earth or the fibrous grass or the hollow tread of the wind.

The buck, all legs dancing nimbly, a faint red mark on his hind, pranced into a wide glade. It was the first warm day of the year. Little birds, their bright breasts held aloft like rising statesmen's, had sung their tunes from dawn, the lark blowing with the first burst of gentle light creeping across the green grass and the rich, brown earth. When the grey sky turned bright, and the dew glistened, the robins, thrushes and wrens bopped from their nests and took their places on the ends of long branches bouncing lightly with the passing breeze. Daffodils, their delicate bouquets shivering with the wind, once drooped with rain, propped up straight like choir boys and waved to the sun. The buck walked across the glade and marvelled at the scene, until he saw on the horizon, fumbling at the ground, a solitary man in a bright orange jacket.

Instinctively the buck broke into a quiet trot, his muscles limbering up for what was to come, his mind loosening. He felt something warm envelop his heart. This was his home. The man turned just as the buck was on him, the short distance between them enough only for his face to turn to dread and his meek voice to call out feebly for a god. The buck dipped his antlers, their sharp tips gleaming, and rammed the man. He fell like a ragdoll on the velvety grass, clutching his flabby chest. The buck circled, pulling up clods of muck and lumps of grass with his powerful legs and tossing his mane of antlers like a bull in heat. The man writhed, first in pain then in fear, weeping and calling unintelligibly for someone or something. He got to his feet, spinning like a lunatic to match the wild canter of the terrifying deer, and held his hands pleadingly in front of him. He tried to coax the buck, but his gentle words were broken by the bitter sobs that ran from him, by the snot that dripped from him, by the garbled phrases that erupted from deep inside him. The buck stopped and the man fell silent, not wanting to disturb what might be a turn of fate. The buck ducked and charged and planted the tips of his antlers in the man's doughy flesh, and when he heard the screams, he kicked all the harder. The man squirmed on the ground, his eyes closed, the life frightened out of him. When the buck pressed his hoof to his chest, he hadn't breath left in his lungs to scream. When the buck eased his weight on, he hadn't tears left to cry. And when he stretched his skin like rubber, and cracked his ribs and tore through his body, the crack breaking through the glade, he hadn't life left to suffer.

Winterbound
by Shelby Schumacher

It's springtime's version of winter's snow
the sakura blossoms start tumbling to the ground
and the autumn of petals let summer know.

My mother asked because she couldn't go,
so I captured an image of the elder trees crowned.
It's springtime's version of winter's snow.

Then she told me a tale with nostalgic gusto
of a towheaded girl who watched, spellbound,
and the autumn of petals let summer know.

The girl swung on the bows of an ancient willow
and scattered the leaves of her imagined playground.
It's springtime's version of winter's snow.

In the depths of my memories, her story did show
within me a childhood that long had drowned,
and the autumn of petals let summer know.

Now I stand amongst the elder trees, that girl aglow;
the crinkle of my timeworn eyes the only sound.
It's springtime's version of winter's snow
and the autumn of petals let summer know.

Tenth Biscuit of the Afternoon
by Jem Braithwaite

I break a biscuit into two halves and position a half in either corner of my mouth. Each half is rounded on its outer side and jagged on its inner. I can see them both in the bottom of my eyesight, and they look, as hoped, like the chocolate-brown pincers of an ant.

I find Harry the dachshund in the kitchen. He looks at me and half-twists his head, maybe hoping to make sense of my pincers by looking at them sideways. He yaps at me, then runs and hides beneath the oven.

"Harry, my love, come out and look at me," I say in a careful mumble, not wanting to damage the pincers. "Don't be a grump now, Harry. You've got to be nice to me today." I get down on my knees and turn my face sideways. There are dark pieces of floor-fluff everywhere, crowded in this under-place like a family of frightened mice. And Harry lies among them. "Out. Now please. You'll get filthy." He is out of my reach, resting his chin on a tennis ball that has grown old back there; its yellow hair has faded to white. Harry's two small eyes are covered in water.

"Oh, I didn't mean to scare you, sweets," I tell him. But as I say this, the pincers wriggle in my mouth, and Harry hides his face behind the ball. I get up from the floor. Maybe Henderson will enjoy my pincers.

I find him lying down at the top of the stairs. He is a huge St. Bernard who sometimes doesn't let me past him, but he is otherwise kind to me. When Henderson sees my pincers, he heaves himself up onto giant paws and barks—but in a nice way. He's playful. I give my nostrils a flaring and move my mouth to get the pincers going. He growls and shows me all the teeth that he uses to tear his food apart.

"There, there, Henderson," I say. He barks at me, then barks again. Loud! He keeps on barking. I ask him to please stop, to please just have some fun and wag his tail, today, for me, and some of my right pincer breaks off, and breaks again on the floor.

He doesn't even come down for the biscuit, just glares, like he wants me to go.

I don't have another dog to visit, so I show myself what's left of my pincers in the bathroom mirror. I do, I look like an ant. I retract and swallow the pincers and feel a bit sick because that's my tenth biscuit of the afternoon. I'm thirty-two. I'm like the tennis ball, fading in the dark.

I think a walk is in order.

Shoes on. Scarf on. Grab leads. *Shake leads*. Shake leads. No sound of paws. Hm, I'll make a real ruckus and rap the metal against the door. *Crack crack*. Nothing. I have upset my dogs. Alone walk then. I hoop the two leads back over their hooks and feel suddenly hollow like two small hands have vanished from my grip. I shuffle to the door and stand on my tip-toes to look through the pane. Out in the road, the traffic moves by in a heaving procession of plastic and metal and rubber and glass. And I don't want to go for a walk anymore.

I drop to my heels and lean against the door.

It doesn't feel stable.

There are tremors in its wood. It is quaking at my touch. My heart has leapt up to a head-booming height. And its shockwaves ride my bones to the floor. The walls seem to shake, the windows to rattle. And the ceiling is quivering like a palm raised above me. It's as if the day's pillars have been blown out of place. And this is the slow, trembling moment before it all comes down—before the day crashes and enters the pile of sad, sad birthdays.

I don't want to go for a walk anymore. But if I stay in this house any longer, I feel like the whole thing will fall down on top of me.

Outside, the sun is lemony and lowering and will soon be orange. If I leave now, I could walk to the hill. I could maybe reach the top in time for when the sun changes into a different fruit.

The way to the hill isn't so pretty. It's just a walk along a roadside, but I'm out of the house. I'm outside, heading for the sun. To my right, the cars power by me and when I look, I see people inside of them, guiding the wheels with their hands. They are so much faster than me. I feel like I'm crawling.

My toe catches the edge of a slab with a crack in its middle, and I nearly go flying.

Eyes on the pavement, Sally. Eyes on circles of gum…grey, white, black. They are like mini illustrations of the moon's different stages, all with different ratios of shadow and light. I find a kind of crescent moon, a half moon, and a moon with boot-marks and a chunk of it missing. They are the ugliest moons I have ever laid eyes on.

Come on, ground. Give me something to look at. There is nothing green growing between the slabs of concrete, no blades of grass to root for.

But what's that circle, shining just there?

It's a splash of water, dazzling with bubbles.

It's somebody's saliva.

That's enough of the ground.

To my left, terraced houses run in a straight line that is split, here and there, by side roads lined with more terraced houses. Smells of cooking sometimes rush from the windows to lock horns with the car fumes and wrestle for space in my nose. But no one seems to be cooking at the moment. So the air is all car fumes. And it makes me feel a bit sick. I pull my scarf up over my nose and think of turning back.

But up ahead, just a stone's throw away, a song starts up, and I quicken my footsteps in disbelief.

It's coming from the cream-coloured house. A family of voices. I stop outside, and my spirits climb to head height — they are singing happy birthday. The chances! I can't see them through the window. They're in a back room. Deep inside the house. But I mouth along anyway. *Happy-birth-day-to… E-li. Happ-y-birth-day-toooo… you.* I blow at the air and soak up the applause. Thank you, thank you. I'll take it.

I turn around, humming.

An exhaust backfires, and I slump and stand abruptly. I hate them. I hate cars.

They are bulls. Bulls. Tearing through our streets.

I close my eyes and rush down to my stomach. Put my brain there, like a child, to calm down in the rise and fall of my breathing. But it's hard to keep it still. There are beasts grumbling in the darkness of my eyelids. Horned monsters that ruined this day forever. My breath's gone missing. I'm in my stomach, searching for the rise and fall. It's my birthday, and I'm in my stomach, listening, waiting, for signs of life. I cannot hear my own breath. It's covered, overwritten. Louder breaths have claimed the air, final and reaching. My brothers are at my sides, breathing again. And their presence seems to have swallowed my own. They announce themselves, again and again, in a series of gasps that stagger the air, while ahead, the stampede accelerates. The beasts gather speed, and a heaving mass of grumbling air fights for space in my ears. And it's as if they hear it too; their breathing changes. It quickens in fright. They are trembling like pillars as the stampede rushes by. I want to unfurl and hold their schoolboy hands, to bind us in a hard chain and stand as triplets again—humans—hard bones armoured in flesh. I want to go back to that first mind of childish beliefs, where I thought people could only die at one-hundred-years-old. But my brothers went like insects beneath a palm. Ants beneath a shoe. And just as quick, the armour slipped from every living thing, and it all became like this—tiny and wavering. Just waiting to be snuffed. Made dark. Blown out. Like birthday candles planted in a cold, sad cake.

I fall back into my stomach, because it's the only way out of this feeling. And when I find my breath again, I hold onto its rhythm with a kind of half-hatred, resenting every rise and every fall, until a tiredness begins to sedate me, and their breathing fades beneath the rise of my own.

When I open my eyes, the sun is a low, low orange.

So I aim my feet towards that fruit, and I'm walking again.

The field at the base of the hill is large, and I cross it while willing the sun to please slow down. There is not much light left, but what remains is pink and coats the crest of the hill in a thin strawberry glaze. The hill is huge and wide, like a broad pair of shoulders in the way of the sun. Almost no light reaches this field. I can just make out the empty white goal frame. We're the only things standing, and I walk between its posts on my way across the grass.

The field begins to bend upwards and become an ever-steepening hill. The crest still has a little pink to it, but the hill is huge and high. My footsteps don't seem to bring me any closer to the top. I tend to take the other way; the incline is gentler. This way is quicker, but it devours my breath. And the crest is losing its colour. At the top, you can usually see the sea on the horizon and the sun—a pink berry—slowly falling in. And this has saved many days from sad endings.

The crest is almost colourless. I have missed today's show.

There is nothing up there but evening now, which isn't much to look at. I don't know where the moon is, and stars never come here. The town light scares them.

I point my feet back down the hill, but don't move.

Dinner when home. Pasta, left over from yesterday. I will sit down at the table in the silence that Harry and Henderson are failing to fill. And the pile will grow a day higher.

I point my feet back up the slope. I'm standing a third of the way up the hill, waiting for something to enter the sky.

Things that fall
by Tamara Raidt

There are two ways of falling.
    Some people fall like autumn leaves:

easily, gently, with the first gust of wind;
    with the greatest nonchalance, the deepest indifference.

Other people – like me – fall like a tree
    that took a century to grow and four men to topple,

taking down all the time-thickened boughs, and when it hits
    the ground: the earth shivers but the forest doesn't grieve.

Feather
by Medha Singh

swivels slowly to the ground
off the sunny terrace
all the way down

hurtles on in its menace
of a life
on this easy, quiet town

no float, neither zigzag
nor wide curl

    drops, drops straight, crowns
downward, whorls a hole
in the thick air

opening a centre
of gravity that wasn't
there. Entering

life's machinery, determined
to enter its fate

at your feet
(where the sun has
drowned) firmly, without
a sound.

Mirage in the Mirror

by Madison Sotos

For most of my life, practicality has operated on me like a chokehold, its fingers constantly clutching at my neck, threatening to close around my throat. It smothers, suffocates, rears up in violent flashes to tear apart any semblance of mysticality. I've become accustomed to this, the feeling of never really being able to breathe freely, of being constantly battered by reality. At the end of June, after a month of near freedom, practicality bared its threatening teeth once again, as I was boarding a boat to leave a little island in the middle of the Aegean.

That month passed mostly like a daze—I was physically present, but in a way, I remained strangely separate from the events happening to me. I saw everything as if watching it through the lens of a camera. Maybe it was the heat that gave everything the effect of seeming unreal, so that nothing really mattered too much. It was a heat that seemed to my American skin distinctively Mediterranean, so dry that the sweat that gathered in the creases and along the smooth surfaces of my body seemed necessary to avoid shriveling up and disappearing, like a robust grape left out to whither. Yes, that heat was like a weighted blanket, lying atop my worries so heavily that they could not rise to the surface of my brain. The land itself seemed to have absorbed the sun's luminosity, which coated everything in an otherworldly glow, even my brain, which went fuzzy and still under that feverish heat.

Yet, as Theo and I rejoined our group on the tiny boat that would take us away from the island, everyone around us seemed discontent. They were hurried, tense, wishing to move quickly onto the next thing. Already the island's atmosphere, its heady effect, had worn off. Or maybe it hadn't had any effect on them at all. They had probably continued to quarrel with one another, become irritated by sunburn, desperately needed the toilet, become bored and longed for air conditioning and television. A mother of two adolescent boys waved sunscreen bottles in their faces, urging them to reapply as they resisted.

Watching them, something seemed to be breaking down around me. The haze of unreality that had enveloped the island, and me within it, was dissolving. Practicality was recommencing its suffocating hold over everyone—the guests in a hurry, the mother and her sons with their sunscreen—and they didn't even know it. A wave of sadness washed over me then, both for them and for myself. I knew that back on the big ferry, reason would recommence its grip over me as well, once we were out to sea, far from the island. I'd soon feel its nails scraping at the flesh covering my airways.

Instead, moving through the Aegean at steady speed, everything continued to appear like a dream. Observing the people around me on the ferry's deck, I experienced an extreme reversal of that feeling that had overtaken me while leaving the island—one I felt nearly all the time. Practicality was nowhere in sight, leaving me to breathe in big gulps of warm air unobstructed.

A young boy blew bubbles from a plastic tube as his parents cheered him on. The bubbles floated up into the early evening light, taking on a rainbow sheen. And then, when you least expected it, they burst as if struck by a pin. The little spheres of soap exploded into tiny showers of light. Two elderly men sat close together near the deck railing. Periodically, one would lean his head on the other's shoulder and the other one would adjust his stance, crane his neck so as to be able to kiss his lover's head. Their silver and black heads pressed together combined to create a salt and pepper effect.

Strong cologne wafted through the air with an equally peppery, pleasant aroma. A woman standing close to the front railing pulled a harmonica out of a small bag and began to play. Her notes flooded the air and their sound took on a quality like honey dripping slowly down through the air, liquifying in the early evening heat.

The woman playing stood in a patch of brilliant sunlight that obscured her face. Stepping slightly to the side, her head blocked out the sun so that her body was outlined with fuzzy gold. Only thendid I recognize her. She'd been in our tour group on the island. I'dtaken note of her because of her odd way of speaking. I'd heard her before I'd seen her. When she spoke, her voice was even and her tone tranquil. But at the same time, every word she spoke seemed sharp, injected with an uncontained energy. The serene, steady quality of her voice, separate from a face, inclined me to believe that its owner would be elderly. But when I'd looked back to see her, I was surprised by brown hair instead of white, and a face that seemed marked only by smile lines. Crinkles created tiny pleats around her eyes and mouth, not yet etched deeply and permanently into folds of sagging skin.

These strange, opposing qualities coexisting within the woman's voice and the contrast between age and youth within her had led me to suspect that maybe she was a spirit of the island. Now I turned to Theo, trying to ascertain that he could see her too, that he could hear the music emanating from the instrument held up to her mouth. He seemed able to see her, and was watching her too. In fact, lots of people on the ferry deck were looking in her direction and had paused to watch her play.

The light around her figure created an ethereal effect, fortifying the impression that she herself, like the island, belonged in a different world, to a different time—a time without time. I thought that I would like to exist without time, without place. Then I could stay forever in moments such as this one.

The woman did not lay out a hat or an instrument case. Several people came up to her and tried to give her money. But she refused them, shaking her head politely no, her eyes smiling while she kept her mouth on her harmonica. If they dropped money at her feet, she would bend down, while still playing, pick it up, and return it to them insistently.

On the ferry ride over to the island, Theo and I had made up stories about fellow passengers: where they were from, where they were going on the ferry, why they were traveling there, what they were doing. We hypothesized their backstories: a silver-haired man standing alone at the railing was a recently retired Argentinian diplomat. He'd come to Greece to celebrate the end of his career, the beginning of freedom. But the vacation and all the leisure time it proffered had an unwelcome effect. With nothing to do all day but sit with his own thoughts, he'd been suddenly accosted by the discovery of his old age and the realization that he did not know how to be with himself alone. So, he'd decided to take a day trip to the little island to visit some of the old churches, in the hopes that by simply occupying that traditionally spiritual space, he'd find some sort of peace. (My story). A pair of middle-aged American women, walking arm-in-arm, were best friends since their childhoods in California. One of them was turning forty-five, so they were on the ferry with Mykonos as their final destination. They were going to relive their lost youths in the clubs and drink themselves into oblivion. (Theo's story).

As I watched her, I tried to invent a story about the woman playing the harmonica, to imagine her a past and a reason for her trip to the little island. But I couldn't—everything I imagined seemed wrong. Too ordinary. Just as she appeared to be without time or place, she appeared also to be without a story, or at least a story I was capable of comprehending. This inability to fabricate an identity for her increased my curiosity.

Theo suggested we move closer to hear the music better. So, we left our little table and he pulled two chairs together, side-by-side. We sat at the edge of the deck behind the musician, our backs to her. We were near the railing, facing out toward the sea, and sometimes the seafoam sprayed upwards and misted us. The notes of her music drifted back towards us and flowed out over the water. After a bit, the sounds of the other passengers' chatter and the rush of the sea crashing up against the ferry were the only ones I heard. I turned in my seat. The harmonica player was no longer on the deck, no longer playing. My eyes scanned the crowd, flitting anxiously, as if to lose sight of her would constitute some great, significant loss. Spotting her finally, gliding past the coffee stand, I breathed a sigh of relief.

Next to me, Theo's eyes were closed. I made my way toward the coffee stand.

The musician had moved on and was disappearing behind the bathroom door just as I reached it. Without a clear aim, I followed. I stood at the sink, examined my skin in the mirror, pleased to see how it had browned in the day. My hair, now plastered to my face with sea water, had lightened. I splashed cold water onto my cheeks and neck, reveling in its coolness. The stall door creaked open behind me. Then came a pleasant whistling, growing louder as its source approached the sink next to me. I dabbed at my eyes with my fingers, leaving the rest of my face dripping, and pretended to examine it in the mirror. Really, I was examining the reflection of the whistler, who was now humming: it was her, the woman with the elderly voice, the harmonica player, the imagined phantom of the island. She smiled at my reflection and went on humming, running her soapy hands under the tap.

Upon closer reflection, her face was not materially so young as it had appeared to me before. She was middle-aged, but most likely on the upper end of the scale—not yet sixty, but maybe nearly there. There was a jovial quality there that confused me, made her appear youthful. Her eyes seemed to radiate a hopefulness that I'd never seen in any person. Her hair was dark brown and violently curly, tinged with gold where the sun had seen it. No thinning or traces of silver marked out her age. Her skin was clearly accustomed to the sun but hadn't acquired that leathery quality so often found in people who've spent their lives laboring or lounging in the uncovered outdoors. The most notable thing about her physical appearance, though, was her eyes, which were two entirely different variants of green. The left was very light and tinged with a cold, crystalline blue, appearing almost silver in places. The right was much darker, speckled with brown and flecks of gold.

Her humming grew louder and more jovial as she continued scrubbing her hands and every once in a while, she let out a little laugh, as if sharing a private joke with herself. When she'd finished, she wiped her hands on her blouse, smiled cheerfully at my reflectionin the mirror, and walked light-footed out the door.

I remained staring at the mirror where my face swam before me, yet the face that remained in my mind was not my own. It was that of the harmonica player. She intrigued me. She seemed to possess some unidentifiable quality that made her instantly stand out, drew me to her. She carried herself with confidence, with a security of self that was unimaginable to me. She possessed an inherent elegance. Her sophistication did not come from her plain clothes or her uncolored hair but again, from something unidentifiable, unnamable. This quality that I couldn't identify was one I wished to possess myself. I would've liked to speak to her, to mimic her intonation, her tones. I would have liked to cultivate a version of myself that aligned with her, to mimic her way of walking and dressing, observe her facial expressions and learn how to reproduce them. I imagined creating a self-portrait that mingled my features with hers, aging me, but also injecting me with that indefinable air. Injecting me with form.

It seemed to me then that I had no solid form, no concrete self. Like a mirage caused by the heat, any singular version of me only shimmered faintly in the air for a moment before revealing itself to be false. While the harmonica player—in voice, expression, and action—existed with radiance and force that could not be denied, I myself was like one of Dali's clocks. My body was melting in the heat, drooping and losing shape and soon I'd be formless, nothing but a series of flesh-colored puddles on the ground. Everything I was, was in between. I could only describe myself in terms of what I was not, which was everything.

Whereas this woman seemed to exist as fully formed as anyone could possibly be. How to become like that? How to become someone?

Without the weight of reality pressing down on me, practicality having momentarily taken its foot off my chest, becoming someone seemed possible to do. Perhaps I could achieve a form, a self that instead of liquifying in the heat would solidify, catch permanently in the air and stay there, like the scent of the sea.

This excerpt is part of a larger coming-of-age novel about a young woman's exploration of the Mediterranean, human relationships, and herself.

The Page is the Source and You are the Stream
by Liam Wright

The grey, unspoken word could only
loom above for

so long.

Now it is
a droplet, now many
downpours of bead-spawn.

They are so quick to become
a multitude of little lives. Nascent

eel-ish things, slick
and flicking in
the cold backdrop.
They flow horizontally

out into

the open.
Appearing before the eyes,
they will thread their way

through

to the cerebrum, taking
that tributary across
to the amygdala, eventually seeping
onto the awaiting tongue.
Here they pile and spill before

leaping

into
another
nearby living estuary, willing
themselves oh-so-slowly

onto the blank again.

Anxiety of Influence:
In Conversation with Harold Bloom
by Heather Dunnett

My pen is influenced by anxiety,
thus it runs with no propriety,
no trust in myself belongs to me.

Still young, fresh, ready for the mould,
not cooled yet to the world, made cold,
maybe this will come when I get old.

In my youth I have no true voice,
experimentation leaves me no choice,
copying Burns, Blake, Whitman, Joyce.

Maybe one day I'll have something to say
that reads unique, in my own way,
maybe one day the people will pay,

to hear my take, to read my seal,
they'll think I have some talent, real
and not just others' style to steal.

Yet building like this is how we make,
nothing original, we poets only take,
to think otherwise would be a mistake.

Inspiration is a question of who and when,
one can only sing of other men:
This is the force that moves the pen.

Helping Hand
by Tamara Raidt

I want a helping hand
male or female
a friendly one
nails cut short
or long.

I need a helping hand
a strong one
not slippery
not sweaty
that has enough
fingers to count up
all my questions.

Hanging to that hand
I need an arm to hold mine,
a shoulder to carry my thoughts
on the safer road home.

I need a someone
who's not a saviour
not a villain,
who makes
the world bearable
for tiny shoulders
with heavy hearts,
who makes
herbal medicine
out of words.

Environ(mental) Impact
by Olivia Thomakos

On our first date, I tore my plastic coffee lid to shreds,
swore next time to request a cup without one. Except then

I don't know what I'd do with my hands. Always fidgeting
with chains fastened around my neck, I accidentally broke

the necklace you made for me. At family dinner
your mother hovers in the kitchen, asks why I am rummaging.

Later you reasoned, *she just doesn't know you yet,*
implying you did. Every pot has a lid,

but these days we feel more like Tupperware,
trying to fit the wrong pieces together.

FaceTime dinner dates cut short by your strict
sleep schedule. When I asked you to dream next to me

you weighed my presence against the Earth
and found I wasn't worth the carbon emissions.

I'd even stretched my truth to fit your taste
at the cost of consuming bacon and brie –

Fuck it. Tomorrow I will walk to the cafe where we met,
order a cappuccino to go, and take a bite

from a warmed ham-cheese croissant because
it's only $3.95 and honestly, the tofu burger sucks.

perfect lipstick on a white ceramic mug
by Heather Dunnett

cherry-red half moon marks the lip of a clean white ceramic.
in school, they used to mark our work in harsh crimson pens,
crossing out the mistakes and highlighting the wrong.
i used to think that lipstick on mugs was my mark on the world
but maybe it is a mark against me,
the harsh red lines circling all of the *wrong*.
stains are not a fixed stand, nor footprints in the sand
easily washed away by gentle tide,
not a sign of greatness, no star on the sidewalk,
just marks to be scrubbed away, *wrong*.
you are trying to be more than a perfectly painted smile,
wanting to be more real, not just doll pink.
you hide behind warrior paint to feel alive
on this battlefield against your own mind.
what good is coffee to perk you up
when your mind is trying to bring you down?
red marks like scratches, wolf claws on snow -
you're bleeding into your coffee again
blood and caffeine on your lips
as familiar as oxygen.
you can clean the ceramic
but you cannot wash the taste away.

Freckles

by Rhiannon Fisher

I hold my hands under the dripping tap, and the water runs thick with blood.

He came at you first, the voice in my head reassures me. Perhaps it is my voice, though I've never sounded so confident before, so sure of myself. *He came at you first, you had no choice.*

The blood is tacky, sticking to my skin as I drag the pads of my fingers across the backs of my hands. I waited too long, sat beside his body too long, stared at the crinkles of his crows feet to avoid looking into his vacant eyes for too long. *You had to make sure he was gone,* the voice says, *you had to make sure he couldn't hurt you anymore.*

I nod. That's right. He hurt me.

And I killed him.

I dig the nail of one thumb under the other, cleaning in careful crescent moons until the beds are soft and pink. I see a glint out of the corner of my eye and whip around, afraid for a moment that somehow he has gotten up, though I watched the life twitch out of him. But it's only a knife, lying on the kitchen floor near his head, catching the light from the bulb swinging gently in time with the air conditioner.

I pause. How did he hurt me? I ask the voice in my head.

He came at you with the knife, it replies. *Don't you remember?*

But I thought I had the knife, I say. I had been making dinner when he walked in, I say. I remember my fingers clenching around the handle, carving valleys into my flesh, I say.

My head pounds, and I twist the tap until the water that comes out is scathingly hot, scalding my skin until it's stinging and raw. When I finally turn it off, the kitchen is silent, silent like a distant door closing in an empty house, silent like a library at midnight, silent like a final exhale.

I close my eyes; the bulb feels too bright now. I try to recall details—time, action, his initial attack—but all I see behind my eyelids is the knife swinging down towards his chest in deadly arcs again and again. All I feel is the jerk of the blade as it caught on his ribs and then slipped between them. All I hear is his sharp intake of breath, the soft grunts of pain as he writhed and wriggled beneath me, one hand clutching the leg of the kitchen table, the other caught in my hair, head thrown back, bottom lip tucked between teeth. Wait. I must be remembering that wrong. He hadn't screamed. He should have screamed.

Why didn't he scream? I ask the voice.

You should clean up, it replies instead. *You'll need bleach for the linoleum. Mix it with four parts water.*

I taste metal on the back of my tongue like I'm going to be sick. I should have been sick already; I'm not good with blood. I can't remember if I've eaten dinner. Maybe I didn't; maybe that's why I haven't thrown it up. I don't know how long I sat with him on the floor as his body cooled, as his blood dried black on the bottoms of my bare feet. It was dark when he came home; it's dark now.

He looks younger in death, the deep furrows of his brow smoothed, limbs splayed out like he's sleeping, jaw slack and open. Maybe he had screamed.

Why did I kill him? I ask the voice, and the calm that had washed over me the first time I heard it is gone.

He was going to hurt you. It sounds impatient now.

I shake my head, slowly, trying to remember, but my mind is fuzzy like TV static, fuzzy like a beer that is all foam, fuzzy like ash left un-swept in a fireplace. He never hurt me before, I say. He was gentle, I say. He kissed me 'hello', I say. I was holding the knife, I say.

I look over the kitchen sink. There's a window there, panes of glass dark and reflective. Blood freckles my skin like molten sunspots. I clutch the edge of the sink, grounding myself in the cool press of porcelain. My head pounds in time with my heart. There is a pressure at the base of my skull.

I study myself in the glass. There is my face—familiar—my nose, my lips, my eyes. I look the same as every other day. Today was a day like every other day. Why would I kill him?

My hand reaches towards my throat, towards my mother's necklace, towards the small silver cross I hold whenever the world feels too much, but I'm grasping at nothing. I look around frantically, but the cross is not on the kitchen counter, it is not near the microwave or the spice rack or the little potted fern he gave me. It is not on the floor beside his rigid body.

I finally spot it just under the sink near my feet. When I reach down to grab it with trembling hands, a sharp pain flares across my palm, and I shriek in time with the voice in my head.

Get rid of it, the voice hisses as I drop the cross into the sink, the metal clanging on the porcelain like a rusted church bell. I examine my hand, biting my lip to keep the tears from slipping. Pressed into my palm is a burn, a burn so intricate I can make out every detail, from the stone in the center of the cross to the delicate chain that always hangs around my neck.

It hurt you, the voice coos in my head, and it feels like the stroking of claws, gentle, but like any wrong move from me, and the voice could pierce the soft gray matter of my brain, shredding it like ribbon. *It hurt you like he hurt you. Get rid of it.*

I find myself brushing the cross across the bottom of the sink to the drain with a spoon. I find myself reaching up and pressing the garbage disposal, shuddering as the gears grind it up, the sound of it like a knife across an empty dinner plate.

When I turn off the disposal, the silence clangs through the room, the air yawning and soaking up the sound like something hungry. It leaves me lightheaded, and I grip the edge of the sink to steady myself.

My gaze moves back to my reflection in the window, from my frizzy hair to the crimson freckles dried and pulling at my skin when I move, to my eyes, too dark and too wide. I see his body behind me, splayed out across the floor, framed in the glass like a portrait by Currier and Ives, the first snowfall of winter dancing through the air outside. He loved the snow, I say, my voice like too-thin ice, cracking when I speak. He loved the snow, I say. He loved me, I say.

And I loved him. What happened?

The voice does not respond.

What happened?! I want to scream it, but my throat is tight like something is blocking the passage. I want to shake myself, but I don't seem to be in control of my limbs. All I can do is stare at the window, the snowflakes gathering on the sill outside.

I feel drowsy, and the pressure at the base of my skull is building to the point of pain. I blink, slow and languid, and when I open my eyes, for just a flash it seems I am no longer looking at myself in the glass. But then I blink again, and it is just me, though something seems wrong about the picture.

Who are you? I ask. There is no reply, but the pounding in my head feels like laughter, playful at first, but then harsh and dark, and the light above my sink begins to pulse like a beating heart. With every flicker my grip on the basin tightens until my fingers ache, until blood pounds between my ears, behind my eyes, until the pain from the burn on my palm makes me nearly sick. Then it stops, the light burning bright, and I breathe again, barely registering the ache in my lungs. I cannot stop staring at his body behind me, too still and too pale. I feel the soft caress of the voice humming in the back of my mind.

My body feels too tight, like skin stretched over the frame of a drum. I want to crawl out of myself and sit on the floor beside him, push his dark hair off his proud brow and kiss the dimples in his cheeks, or maybe run out the front door screaming, but I cannot seem to move either way. My body feels as stiff as his, like it is possible I could never move again.

Do not worry, the voice says, soft like satin; soft like a raindrop on a rosebud; soft like a lover's whisper between cool sheets. *I am here now. I am here, and he will never hurt you again.*

But, I hurt him, I manage to say, my jaw clenched so tightly I think perhaps my teeth will shatter. My voice is too soft for anyone to hear, if there was anyone here to listen. I know it is the truth now, though I do not remember.

My hands are sticky again. When I look down, the right one clutches the bloody knife so tightly that my knuckles turn pale like the pages of a book, pale like bleached bone, pale like a fresh corpse. I do not remember moving across the kitchen floor. I do not remember picking up the knife from where I'd left it near his head. I do not remember coming back to the sink. It is still dark, but the darkness looks different, like maybe time has passed, though I could not say how much.

I look back at my reflection in the window. Some of the blood has started to peel off of my face, leaving black flakes against the white sink, gathering like the snowfall outside.

When I speak, it is like talking underwater, everything heavy and in slow motion. You made me hurt him, I say.

The silence is deafening. When I smile, it is not my smile.

My Eve
by Amy Curtis

I chase the sunset through the sky all afternoon:
a slow-burning seduction, hoping she likes me too.
Sometimes she's shy, only peeks with smoky eyes,
but tonight her amber glow is sanguine.

I hoped to see her rosy blush fill the clouds,
and for the sweetest moment, I do. Her peach lips
kissing the sea like a lover, a golden halo hovering above:
an angel slowly sinking in the sky.

I marvel her at cherry-tinted goodbye: seeing her fade
into an evening slumber. She leaves me alone
in street light shadows, my loneliest hour
when she slips under the covers.

I hear her stained-glass whisper like a promise,
my wet eyes shining brighter than the stars.
Her brief lipstick print brushes across the heavens,
my blushed cheek captures her kiss.

The Ottoman

by Annie Bashaw

Geoffrey has something to tell Irene. He's bought yellow chrysanthemums. He's phoned ahead. He's even prepared a speech. He's tried to be ready—oh, he's tried. Yet his shoulders tense at the thought of knocking on her door, at being invited inside. His stomach twists at the prospect of being offered tea and saying his piece. He's avoided this conversation for a while now.

Antsy, he stops at the corner bodega to buy her biscotti. He doesn't know if she likes biscotti, but her husband, Wesley, does— if she doesn't eat it, perhaps she can save it for him. He gives exact change to the bodega owner and sets off down Lexington Avenue. He'll walk the seven blocks to her building and take the elevator to the eighth floor. He'll knock on 812, quietly, so he doesn't disturb Yonzo the Doberman in 811. Though, he thinks perhaps he should disturb Yonzo the Doberman, so Yonzo's loquacious owner will open the door, chat his ear off for a quarter of an hour while Geoffrey scratches Yonzo behind the ears, and delay his conversation with Irene.

His fantasies flutter away when he sees the door to 812 already propped open wide. Geoffrey brushes his boots on the forest green doormat and enters.

"Mrs. Lewis?" he calls.

Soft jazz drifts from a stereo and tickles his ears. The apartment is light and airy. Geoffrey wanders into the living room and picks up a framed photo of Wesley and Irene from a shelf otherwise filled with books. Wesley is wearing his usual outfit: a turtleneck and square, gold-rimmed glasses. It's a stylish look that Geoffrey has brazenly adopted.

He replaces the frame and examines the room for the first time during the day, light filtering through sliding glass doors. A law student with a budding interest in interior design, he approves of the gauzy curtains, modern art fixtures, and the hardwood floor.

The only color comes from the deep green sectional and a round ottoman where the coffee table should be. The ottoman, with its button-tufted top and pleated skirt, is the vilest grandma-floral fuchsia he's ever seen.

Geoffrey almost gags. Why would anyone choose to ruin the elegant décor with such a horrid piece? Wesley would never choose something so outrageous. It had to be the work of—

Irene. He hears footsteps and turns to see her in the doorway behind him. Her thin lips cast an amused smirk. She looks well put together, wearing a turtleneck sweater and velvet pants.

They met once before, a couple months back, when she accompanied Wesley to a law function awarding the Reyes Law Fellowship to Geoffrey. She looks as she did then, with the same bob, dyed black and cut just below her ears, almost too short. Striking, yet chic.

"Geoffrey, my dear. Welcome."

"Mrs. Lewis." He holds out his hand, hoping she won't judge it for its clamminess.

She doesn't take it. "Call me Irene."

"I picked these up for you," Geoffrey says. He holds out the flowers and biscotti.

"Biscotti? Did Wes tell you it's my favorite?" The corners of her lips turn down, but her frown conveys pleasant surprise. She takes the offering. "I'll get you some tea, and we can split it. Shall we sojourn in the kitchen?"

She doesn't give him time to answer. Irene leads him to the kitchen, where light warms the natural wood features. Not a speck of dust nor a crumb of food dull the sleek appliances or smudge the granite countertops. Its cozy, inviting atmosphere only amplifies his guilt.

A counter-height table sits against one wall. On one side, a laptop rests on two thick books, surrounded by writing utensils, a glasses case, and papers with highlighted print under images of paintings and sculptures.

"Have a seat. I have someone coming imminently, but they won't infringe for long."

As Irene breezes by, she slides the laptop and papers to the side. She sets the flowers and biscotti on the counter before disappearing through the doorway behind the table.

Geoffrey slides into a seat at the edge, practicing his speech in his head. He bounces his leg and wonders if he's nervous or impatient or both. Probably both.

Irene returns with a vase and arranges the chrysanthemums. She boils water for tea and plates the biscotti. Finally, she slides into the seat across from him.

"To what do I owe the pleasure?" She looks at him down her aquiline nose with narrowed, focused eyes.

Geoffrey attempts to speak but realizes his speech is already messed up. In practice, he'd addressed it to Mrs. Lewis, not Irene.

Just how many changes to his meticulously memorized monologue would he have to make? He tugs at the neck of his turtleneck, a nervous tick.

"M—Irene, there's something you should know. I—"

He flinches when an alarm goes off, obtrusive dings patterned in fours.

"So sorry. That would be the tea." Irene kills the timer before bringing the teapot to the table. She strains tea into two mugs. "I'm sure you like Pu-erh. It's smoky. I find it delightful with biscotti." Immediately, she plunges the almond cookie into her cup.

Geoffrey takes the second of the pair and does the same. He doesn't know if the bite will be hot, so he blows on it just in case, which makes Irene laugh. He sheepishly averts his eyes.

"It's particularly nice after a run," she says.

They're getting off track. He's come here to come clean and that's what he's going to do. He's going to deliver his speech.

"You run?" Geoffrey asks and mentally kicks himself.

"I'd never get any exercise otherwise. When you're my age,

you have to stay in shape."

"Do you ever feel tense afterwards?" He adjusts his glasses. "I haven't been able to stretch out much lately." He needs to stop delaying. It only magnifies his nerves. He needs to tell her.

"Oh, my dear. All the time. Let me recommend you to my massage therapist, she works wonders," Irene says, moving to the counter where she's left her phone. "Everyone must have a massage therapist. You won't be young forever. Better to start early."

"Thank you, but I'm not sure I can afford it. Anyway, Irene, there's something—"

"She'll give you a discount. If it's still too much, the first one's my treat."

Geoffrey pulls at his turtleneck again. He isn't here to make friends. Quite the opposite, in fact.

"That's too kind of you."

"Sent. She'll contact you." Irene smiles and slides back into her seat. "Anyway, what were you saying, my dear?"

Geoffrey looks at his tea and decides to throw her name out of the speech entirely. "There's something you should know. I'm in lo—"

Irene's laptop pings, catching her attention. "One moment, my dear."

She opens the glasses case and pulls out square glasses before typing, slightly hunched with concentration. Instinctively, Geoffrey pushes his own glasses up the bridge of his nose, embarrassed to match her. He wonders if Irene and Wesley share glasses or simply wear the same style. He decides to eat his biscotti without dipping it into the scalding tea and the sound of his gnawing accompanies the low jazz music. In the space of waiting, his fear of confessing has room to grow.

"So sorry. I work as the personal art curator for a wealthy individual in the city. I can't tell you who it is. He likes his privacy. It might be Robert De Niro. It's not him, but I'd like people to think it is. But it's not him. I wish it was."

"What does a personal art curator do?" Geoffrey asks, bouncing his leg again. He's mildly interested—he knows nothing about art, a glaring gap in his budding hobby. More than that, though, he wants to delay his speech. She's thrown him off—he needs time to recover.

"Mostly I take him to the Whitney, sometimes to the Museum of Modern Art, and he points out what he likes. Then I find something similar, usually an original. If he likes the artist, I'll also arrange private showings."

Geoffrey wonders if Irene also chose the art for the apartment. Perhaps that's why, every time Geoffrey comes over, Wesley is so particular about how they leave the place. The art is not to be disturbed. The wine glasses are to be washed, dried, and re-racked. The white throw, folded twice, is to be draped over the green couch. And most importantly, the bed is to be made.

He wonders if the ugly ottoman is an artistic choice and tries to find a way to ask about it.

"Did you do the art for this apartment?"

"Just a second." Irene finishes typing, then shuts the laptop and takes off her glasses. She takes a sip of her tea, sighs contentedly, and gives him her full attention. "I chose the art and furniture and arranged it all, my dear. I did everything."

"Did Wes—Professor Lewis choose anything?"

"No, no. How could he? He doesn't have an eye for the aesthetic."

So she had chosen the ottoman. Relishing her admission and his cleverness, Geoffrey takes a sip of his tea. It's piping and he sputters; he puts the cup down.

"I see. I guess his fashion sense doesn't translate to interior design."

Irene's eyes scrunch with amusement. "Fashion sense? I'm afraid that's my doing, too. He'd wear sweats if I didn't buy his clothes. I think he looks dashing in a turtleneck."

Geoffrey looks at his biscotti crumbs in shock. He thought he was taking after Wesley. How much of Irene has influenced him?

No. It doesn't matter. He's smitten. The first time Geoffrey saw Wesley, he was in the law library deciding whether to apply for law school. He knew it was love at first sight, and his desire to encounter the enigmatic professor in his courses cemented his decision. Wesley was quite the opposite to Geoffrey—always late, bad with technology—but opposites attract. Geoffrey loved how Wesley listened to him talk about interior design, his childhood, anything. Wesley didn't like to talk about himself, but he did teach Geoffrey sudoku, and when they weren't entangled in each other, they could play for hours, heads together, working on the hard ones.

What can Geoffrey do but tell his partner's wife and hope she'll understand? Enough distractions. He must get back to his speech. He opens his mouth to speak.

"How do you find law school?" Irene asks.

Geoffrey forces a smile and imagines flipping the table. "It's good. I'm really enjoying it."

"Excellent. Do you know what type of law interests you? I know you're only a one-L."

"I'm thinking patent or copyright law."

"And you came here for my advice?"

"What? Sorry if this sounds rude, but do art curators know much about law?"

Irene narrows her eyes before clarity effaces her confused expression. "I think you've misunderstood something. I became an art curator because I achieved everything I wanted to achieve as a lawyer. The fellowship you earned is my fellowship. My name is Irene Reyes, not Irene Lewis. I thought you were being funny when you called me that earlier."

Geoffrey clutches his half-empty teacup. "But aren't you two—"

"Married? Yes. I kept my last name." Her amused smirk returns. "Did you come here to tell me you're sleeping with my husband? I already know. Wes tells me everything."

Geoffrey drops the teacup. It clatters on its saucer and tea splashes onto his sleeve.

Irene doubles over with laughter, nose inches from the table. Geoffrey can feel heat flush his face. He jumps up to leave, then jumps again—hostile barking sounds from the hallway, followed by an insistent, "*Yonzo! Shush!*"

"'Scuse me? I'm here to pick up an ottoman?" a voice calls from down the hall.

Irene wipes tears from her eyes. "Geoffrey, my darling, have a seat. I'm just selling Wesley's old ottoman and then we can continue our chat."

The jazz music puts him in a trance. He wonders if she'd leave Wesley, if Geoffrey asked. He wonders how much of her would leave.

He hears the door shut. When she returns, Geoffrey has finished choking down his tea.

"Ugly thing. I've tried to convince Wes to get rid of it for years." She slides back into her seat and dunks the remnants of her biscotti.

Geoffrey says nothing. He trains his eyes on his empty mug and thinks about how he hadn't known what biscotti was until Wesley introduced it to him, nor had he run a day in his life until Wesley suggested he take up the sport. Wesley never even exercised.

Irene sighs.

"I see I've made you uncomfortable. You should know, I don't mind at all. My marriage to Wes is completely platonic. We're best friends, that's it. We even have separate bedrooms. More tea?" Irene flips the switch on the kettle. "I do hope you come around more. I think we'd get along. Wes told me he got you into sudoku. It's my favorite game."

veronica
by Amy Curtis

she licks off her lipstick like
it's strawberry jam: pretending
pretty things must taste sweet;

drinking coffee for aesthetic
but up anxious all night – only warm
milk sends her to sleep.

she wears butterfly socks beneath
smart-casual shoes, smoking
cigarettes that taste like mint;

reads teen magazines on her way
to the office, believes she's worth
more if she shrinks.

inviting men over for a glass of wine
fooling around on her childhood bed.
only kissing, teddies hidden,

some girls just pretend to be women.

Face Machine

by Syed Ahmed

'That's too much for a frame,' Adnan observed. 'I don't want it. That's far too much.'

'How about just pasting and laminating?' Aslam Chagani suggested.

'There you go, Adnan. Go for Lasani wood. That's the new thing,' his brother Manzoor suggested. 'We have pictures pasted on cardboard and a clear plastic sheet fused on top. Look, here's what we've done for someone.'

'And,' Adnan interrupted, 'you've screwed a plastic prop onto the back. Not bad. So how much for that?'

'For you friend, only two hundred,' said Manzoor.

'It is fifty rupees at Jamia Cloth on Burns Road.'

'Then have it done there, why don't you?'

'Make it one hundred.'

'No. Two. That's it!'

'Aslam Bhai, I'm going to Burns Road, okay.'

'No issue, Adnan, go. By all means, go.'

There was heavy traffic on the road. The half-bald man who had served Adnan potato bun-kababs for lunch stood busy, pressing down buns on a thick hot plate. Adnan had got off where there was a chance of him not being recognised after sixteen years: his father still owed money to businesses in the market. He found himself in a bazaar, settling for a kiosk on wheels. The frames there were gaudy, not of the kind he was likely to buy. But of course, people needed frames, even gaudy ones–people had bare walls to cover–they needed frames to hook or hang on nails.

Adnan walked on, his pictures in a large brown envelope, taking in the makeshift roadside cabins that looked like encroachments. He stopped at a hole in the wall: a shop made of brick, painted in dark green. A young man sat on his haunches, ears sticking out, sipping tea. He noticed Adnan's envelope, and his eyes widened. His younger brother, the man's spitting image but with bigger eyes, lifted his chin and exclaimed, 'Yes, sir! What are you looking for?'

'Yes, sir, what would you like' the elder of the two echoed. Adnan decided he would look elsewhere.

An elderly man, who Adnan noticed watching him from behind, jumped into the fray.

The old man had one foot upon his chair. Adnan could see the grimy tassels of his kamarbund. Struggling to release his foot, he lowered it and fumbled for the slipper. He got up, waddled towards Adnan, and came to stand very close.

'Ssa-ma leikum,' he said. Adnan felt drops of spit land on his face. Three teeth were missing. Years of tobacco had yellowed his gums, and he could see the grimy tassels of his kamarbund. Adnan held the forefingers the man had offered him. 'What size are the pictures?'

Adnan held up the khaki envelope. '8 by 10.'

'Come, I've got another shop a little further up this way.' The old man pointed to the other side of the road and said, 'By the way, I have another shop there too.'

Adnan was not able to make much out of it. There was bluish smoke and dust billowing between the vehicles, so many of them that one would never be able to walk across the sixty feet except on an empty road holiday. It was almost as if he was looking through a prism of rising hot gases, creating an impression of translucence. Clouds of soot rose from the exhaust pipes of buses, smothering the neem trees. Adnan could see why the bark of the neems seemed to have burnt sienna warts: somehow, they survived the carbon rain. So did the cabin keepers.

Adnan followed the old man. He stared at the dewlaps above the scruff of his neck, the shaven head and white prayer cap. A large bus passed, fumigating them with a hosepipe emitting burning plastic smoke. The man seemed accustomed to the leaky seals of the engines.

Adnan stepped on the old man's heel. He stopped, turned around, annoyed, suddenly smiled and carried on. Adnan apologised. The old man carried on walking, eyes fixed on the road. They stopped at a cement cabin. The old man stepped onto a chair and climbed into his shop. He set down the photographs on the workbench, turned a silver key in a green strongbox, pushed the hatchback, and turned towards Adnan with a smile, saying, 'You can take them the day after tomorrow.'

Adnan drew out his wallet and handed the old man the money. The old man's mouth hung open as he hunted for change in the box, still gaping as he produced it.

'Don't you worry; you've got the best deal.' His chest heaved as he added, 'Your pictures will not ever yellow. We don't use cheap gum or plastic.' In his zeal, he had begun to lisp. He turned to the pictures and grinned.

'Is this Europe?' he asked, glancing at Adnan.

'No, Amreeka.'

'Which state?'

'Pennsylvania.'

'You're looking very nice,' the man said with a nod, examining his pictures.

He looked up at Adnan and smiled with abandon, revealing the missing three-tooth gap. Ravines, Karakorum foothills, a river delta below the crow's feet showed up on the reassuring face.

'I was once young too.'

He slowly raised his hand and pointed to a frame of simple wood and glass enclosing a black and white picture on the wall. It was a serious-looking, simply clothed young man without a cap, top shirt-button open to reveal a talisman on black, neck-clinging lace.

'How handsome I was. Even the women thought so,' he added hurriedly.

Adnan looked at the young man in the picture. The outlines of the eyes and eyebrows had been charcoaled over; the cheeks and lips were pencilled in with pink chalk. There was a moustache, slightly trimmed above the lip.

'You must have been a charmer.' Adnan smiled at him

'I was.'

'Who were those women? What were they like? Just like the ones we see today?'

'Hmm.' The old man looked up while counting the rupee notes in his box, stopping to perch a carpenter's pencil behind an ear and staring straight ahead at the road.

'Simpler women. They did not talk so fast. Or so much.'

'There must have been Hindu Pathans in Peshawar then. Not there anymore.'

'Sikhs, Muslims, Hindus. All.'

'Married or single?'

The old man coughed a little.

'Other people's wives? Admirers?'

'Yes.'

'How did you meet them? In British India?

'I was a milkman, delivering to their doorstep. Those days, women wore chaddars, not burqas. Some of them talked.'

'You must have picked up Pushto there.'

'I've forgotten quite a bit of it. I'm from Bareilly, you see. They were curious about me being an outsider.'

'Did you meet women anywhere else?'

The old man nodded.

'Where,' asked Adnan, 'in Peshawar?' He tried to fathom the impossible.

'In the fields. Behind bushes.'

'Fields and bushes in Peshawar? Who were better - the Sikh women?'

He stared, blinked and declared, 'They were all good. Everyone was different.'

'That's the way it is now.'

'Well, nothing has changed. Yet everything has.' The old man paused. 'You know what has changed? My face. It's not as ruddy and angular as it used to be like yours is now.'

'Well, we can always go back to your picture.'

'You see, it's like this–I fell on my face. Was knocked down crossing this road; broke my jaw in two places. This was a year-and-a-half ago. Look carefully, you'll see that I have a wire cutting across the bones of half of my face.' The old man stopped for a moment. 'I'm lucky to have a face at all.' He slackened his jaw to allow Adnan to inspect the curvature of his face. It was round–like a bucket handle.

Two women, heads and shoulders covered, walked in. The man greeted them respectfully. One had a large plastic bag with green and pink manila file folders inside.

Adnan imagined his pictures in the old man's frames adorning his bedroom wall. He peered at the finish on a frame in the shop that appeared to be wood, but it was a cheap plastic knock-off. There were other gaudy, gilded photograph frames on display, also in plastic. Things they still could not plasticise were the screws, the nails, the nuts, the bolts.

'The whole world rests on nuts and bolts.' The words were meant for the old man, though Adnan did not expect him to know or care.

'If those were gilded plastic, you would not sleep at night.'

A book of short stories in which we are brought face to face with the disadvantaged, disaffected, the alienated, and the marginalised, in Karachi, Pakistan.

Progenitor

by Liam Wright

,

Origin   .

around us,   *You teach*   *

somewhere.   ,

*   .   *wonder*   ,

Isolator,   *and fear*   *

and conjoiner   ;

)◇ *To us all*   mass of trillions,   )◇   ;

.   ◇(*of us all.*   centillions,   ., ◇(   )◇

*   )◇

.

//   as one   .

,   calling   *   *

◇(*I envy*   us all.   ;

,   .

*   *Those*   Feel its pull,   ;

)◇   ,   an overwhelming,

submerging want   ,   ;

.   to see it fall   *like you*   ;

,   .

*   and rise   *who know*

.   and rise   )◇   )◇   ,

;   to form walls   ;//

that never   *know how*   ◇(

;   cease to march and   *to dance*   ;

*.   . *.,   sink   *.*//*   ;.

)◇   °   *with the moon.*

;   *The words we use*   back to the swell.   °

°   Patient maker   °   ;

)◇ ◇(*to hate and love*   of no desire   °

,. ◇(° *flow back to you.*   will reclaim all.   *   )◇

;

Mortal
by Medha Singh

Illness, a dream, a Stygian guard –
the boatman wades toward me, soft-spoken,
well-mannered, 'imperially slim', calls himself
Utnapishtim.

Here, a eucalyptus tree, quickly filling up
with parrots, beside it, a dead sentinel
with white branches

stands, sheared
by time, a lone hawk
at its summit.

Slugs

by Britney Waldrop

You are mid-dream when you are awoken by a rabbit biting your neck. The rabbit stares at you with yellow eyes, pupils shaped like rectangles. Blood slips down the folds of the rabbit's small chin as it hops away, leaving a trail of red seeping into the pink dirt.

'You are not worth consuming.' The words came from somewhere deep within, the liver perhaps.

You assume it is still a dream and close your eyes.

*

When you wake up, the moon is red. Your heart squeezes. You close your eyes, hoping for the familiar white, almost yellow, orb. It stays red. Your throat burns and you want Miller, Smirnoff, Coors, anything, but your body won't move. You can feel your heart and liver and the particles of your lungs, but you can't feel your skin touching the air.

Out of the corner of your eye, you see movement, a pond. It is a deep yellow and smells like urine left to fester. Two eels flip and bite and tug. They make the moon shiver.

You want to go back to when the moon was white, and ponds were a bluish-green that you always found disgusting.

You croak out, 'Clair?'

Then more softly, 'Becks?'

Something that sounds like a frog croaking is the only response.

*

Your eyes are closed, and you barely remember. Flashes go through your mind– red lights in a bus, the people around feature-less, washed out; wind and sun against your skin, your arm hairs dancing in the breeze; a heart-shaped birthmark on a woman's back, your fingers tracing it; fairy lights around a tree; the burn of whiskey down your throat. You try to string it together, to remember what these images mean.

You open your eyes. You expect to see a white light. It takes a minute for them to focus. There is a red moon above you. You can't place why it seems wrong. You close your eyes again. A new flash of images cross your mind—the smell of burnt popcorn; a cat nibbling your fingers, the tongue rough; braiding a little girl's hair, the hair slipping through your fingers, her turning around laughing, mouthing something; sitting in a circle, a green metal disk in your hand, a man saying something you can't hear, a black book open on your lap. Your throat aches and your cheeks flush with the effort of remembering. You blink. The stars, they almost look like fairy lights.

You begin to feel your toes, ankles, fingertips, hair follicles. They vibrate like they have fallen asleep and are just now waking up. There is a cold metal ring on your left hand.

You push yourself up on your elbow. You are in a small clearing full of purple grass and pink dirt. The woods are a deep blue. The left side of your purple button-down is darker. A deep purple stain is spreading, covering the breast pocket. You press your hand into it. It is warm and sticky, and you close your eyes before looking at it.

In the moon's glow, the liquid transforms from crimson to garnet to ruby to merlot to scarlet. You put your finger in your mouth. It tastes almost rotten, like iron and eggs and despair. You spit the blood out. You wonder if that is why the rabbit only took one bite.

You lie there watching the two eels writhing, twisting together. The entangled bodies remind you of watching slugs as a kid, how the two would become one, their sticky residues merging. This is the first memory that you can grasp. You try to hold on to it, repeating the word 'slugs' in your mind.

Slugs. Slugs. Slugs. Slugs. Slugs.
Slugs. Slugs. Slugs.
Slugs. Slugs.
Slugs.
You watch the eels and try to remember something.

*

You wake up with the faint memory of a little girl in a light blue ballerina costume. She glows a soft yellow, a spotlight just on her. Something behind your belly button squeezes. You cling to the memory, trying to keep the little girl's face in your mind. You open your eyes. You never think of the little girl again.

There is a bite missing from your neck, a thick trickle of blood slugging down into the dirt below you. You blink. There is a flash of something when you close your eyes, a sense of light, then it is gone. You look down, and your fingers are coated in something dark. You know it is slug residue. It drips into the forest floor, the slime melting into the dirt and blood below you. You look around for the slugs but find nothing.

'Slugs,' you whisper the word, hoping you'll remember why it feels important. Your stomach clenches, and excrement leaves you.

Your eyelids feel heavier and heavier.

*

You wake up hours later with the moon in the same place, the eels still fighting, and the trees still blue. You lie on the damp forest floor, listening to the water move and the frogs croak. Pink dirt seeps into your scalp, and ants crawl in-between your toes. Your clothes are gone, and your skin glows red in the moonlight. There is air on your neck. You know you should remember something.

You close your eyes and turn to your side, pulling your legs up into your stomach, your arms around your shins. There is a fallen log on the edge of the forest. It is covered in mushrooms, with only a sliver of the deep blue wood peeking through. The mushrooms are fluorescent, neon pinks mixing with vibrant oranges and technicolor yellows. You close your eyes and see the fuzzy outline of a mushroom on a woman's shoulder. The tattoo is next to a heart-shaped birthmark. You feel something behind your belly button. Water leaks from your eyes, mixing into the pink dirt, making globs of dark fuschia.

You stare at the mushroom long after you have forgotten the woman.

You get up, and look down at ants snaking up your legs. There are hundreds of them, their bodies overlapping. They are something close to green. You slide a silver ring off a finger on your left hand and give it to the ants.

You walk and walk and walk. The ground is wet, sinking with each step. You pass a horse drinking from the pond, an armadillo lying down, and hornets swarming a blue leaf.

You circle the pond again and again until you see the body in front of you. It is lying in the clearing, staring at the sky. You sit on its stomach and pick up the right arm. Your tongue closes around the finger, fitting into the dips and grooves, tasting the dried sweat and dead skin of human flesh. Your tongue massages the knuckle, saliva coating the flesh, and then you bite. The finger detaches easily.

The flesh is chewier than you expected. The blood coats your mouth, slipping down your chin, back onto the body below you. You chew and chew and chew. The body's eyes blink.

There are boars and deer and elephants and wolves around the body now, nibbling, chewing, swallowing. Butterflies slip into the body's ears, bunnies swallow the crooked teeth, and a bear pulls off the earlobe. You lick from the arm to the chest. You suck the body's unhardened nipple, pulling and tugging until blood rushes down your throat. The nipple rips off in your mouth. You chew, and the flesh breaks apart. There is a sliver caught between your back teeth. You flick your tongue to get it out.

Arteries burst, and blood pours out of the open chest, and for a moment, you pause. It has gold flakes and silver stars and every color of glitter mixed in. It shines. You slip your tongue between the muscles and ligaments, shifting them with your teeth. The blood is not like yours—it is not too sour. It tastes sweet, warm, comforting. You feel their blood seeping into your own veins, warmth spreading through you, glitter clogging your arteries.

When the bones, pink and slick, are all that is left, you gather them with the others. You make a pile, mixed with wet leaves and sticks. A fire emerges, licking and coating the bones. Emerald fire shifts in the light of the red moon and stars. The rain hits the fire, making it stronger, brighter, changing the color even more.

The bones melt, yellow and white becoming green and blue. The fire flashes a bright pink, and for a moment you feel lighter, and tears run down your face. The heat dries the liquid as it falls down your face. Your skin tightens, and the animals around you shine, the pink of the fire and the red of the moon mixing together.

Then the fire is gone and you move with the rest, scooping the still-boiling gelatin off of the sticks and leaves. It slips between your fingers as you raise it to your mouth. The goop burns as it goes down, and your esophagus melts. The gelatin is chewy. Warmth spreads inside of you, through your stomach and liver and lungs, and you know your blood is heating, boiling, the impurities and the sourness melting away.

You lie down, grass brushing the back of your neck, dirt slipping in between your ass cheeks. The fairy-light stars are different. There is a new light, next to the red moon, a bright pink that matches the color the fire burned earlier.

*

The ants are gone when you wake up. You rise, and pink dirt falls down your body. There is a slug resting between your toes, nibbling on the skin. A thin trickle of blood begins to sneak out. It shimmers blue and gold.

You stare at the yellow pond. The eels are wrapped around each other in a loving embrace, trying to get closer and closer together. The yellow water shifts around them. You watch them for a while, waiting to see if they merge into one. They remind you of slugs. The reflection of the red moon and the tiny stars shift with the ripples.

You walk to the edge of the pond. The blood between your toes mixes with the yellow liquid. You feel your blood leaving, the liquid entering, your body being filled up with bile and semen. You wade further into the yellow water, letting it swallow your feet. They feel like they have disappeared, becoming a part of the pond.

You continue wading. Yellow liquid floods into your mouth. The tongue expands, filling your mouth with urine and excrement and blood and pus. It slides into your ears, tickling your cheeks and seeping into the concaves of your jaw. The back of your throat warms a little, and liquid slips from your throat into your glittery blood, seeping through the holes in your esophagus. Your body begins to disappear: the toes are no longer distinct, the arch of the foot has collapsed. Legs are gone, hips disintegrated, palms split open. You might have cried or defecated or bled or spit. You are bodiless, baptized in the fluids of the world.

You can see the eels fighting in front of you. They are long and thin, a deep black. Their bodies are intertwined, and you can barely tell them apart. You reach out to touch one, and you go right through it. You emerge slowly from the pond, liquid clinging to you. Your body reappears piece by piece—the bulbs of your hair in your scalp, the thin scar on your forehead you don't remember how you got. Your nipples return, hardened and stiff. Your blood reforms, back full of glitter—not just red or blue but turquoise and mauve and magenta.

You fall asleep half in the water, letting it wash over your legs.

*

You wake up lying on your back, the pond consuming you and then spitting you back up. The yellow and orange and white shifts, waves moving up and down your body. You hear the eels slithering into each other. You blink. The black sky, the red moon, fairy lights, a yellow star brighter than the rest. You stay there.

You wait for them to arrive, with your eyes half-open and your body half-covered. Mucus and saliva coat you again and again. A crow flies above you, circling, then lands on your neck, claws puncturing your throat. You blink. He pecks your eye and caws. You can only see half the world now.

Something drags you out of the pond, turns you on your side. The dirt sticks to your lower half, grass tickling the back of your knees. You notice the log with the mushrooms, the pink one with purple swirled in. You watch it ruffle and wave. A rabbit appears and begins smelling your neck. Teeth rip off the skin just below your armpit. It is a nibble, gentle and piercing. Ants sneak between your toes. They swallow your legs again. Tongues tickle the layers of your skin, and teeth tear away your nose. You blink your one working eye. The mushroom seems to be smiling.

There is a chorus of chewing and sucking, and slurping. Slugs wrap around your fingers. They glide up your arm, leaving a thin coat of slime. A turtle rips off your nails. Someone sucks away your eyeballs. You still feel the teeth and tongues, the probing fingers, the bodies sitting on you. They nibble your bones as they build a fire. Warmth surrounds you, and everything that is you burns hotter and hotter. Colors mix together. You are the emerald green, the yellow, the red, and then, you are a flash of white.

The Curtain Falls
by Heather Dunnett

Struck match fizzles to life, before it is blown out
by the ghosts that still lurk. We never did let them out to play,
not our fault that death walked the world
and we had to put the bodies to bed.
I feel their loss like a mourning veil. I look to my own corpse,
the one I tried to reanimate,
but Shelley left no instructions.

I think I did a good job. I think
I did everything I was meant to but still,
there was no lightning. The fire was only a fuse,
extinguished, blown out, oxygen stolen
like a blanketed spotlight, like a curtain falling
heavily on an empty stage, lying in wait
to rise. I hold my hopes in the ashes,
praying the spotlight will shine one day.
The curtain is so heavy as it falls. A tree in the forest.

The curtain never lifts.

Misunderstanding
Chandeep Wijetunge

I felt nothing when I was shot. Maybe my mind was too busy trying to piece together what had happened.

I saw them on my way to the locker—two young men standing at the gym's entrance, arms folded and looking about the place. New cleaning staff? was what I thought. They couldn't be members, in their cheap shirts that were so bright they hurt your eyes, and their cuffed denims and slippers. They looked so small I felt I could crush them with my bare hands. They had to have noticed me: tattoos, muscles, and a haircut they couldn't afford. I couldn't have imagined that in a few moments the same two men, who for an instant had made me feel so glad of my own circumstances, had made me think of my degrees, of the money I was making and the women I was seeing, would jump the turnstile; that they'd produce two handguns that looked as if they'd been put together from old scraps of metal and start pointing them about. Everyone stop what you're doing, put your belongings aside and form a line, they said in calm, business-like voices. The old man who looked like Ron Jeremy, who always ran without losing any weight, almost fell off his treadmill, an event that under different circumstances might've made me chuckle.

At once I obeyed. Why wouldn't I? Their faces were too young, too innocent to convince me that I would lose anything more than a few dirty thousand-rupee notes that lay in my wallet like a multi-layered snake. Educated faces. Reasonable faces. They'd take everyone's money and leave. It was the only outcome that made sense.

I dropped my bag and, arms raised, looked the one in the pink shirt in the eyes. I gave a nod to acknowledge his upper hand and confirm my submission, letting him know that he could count on me to follow his instructions and that if there would be any trouble, it certainly wouldn't come from me. The man, who must have been in his early twenties, whose hair had too much gel or some other nasty thing in it, returned my nod and, casually, as if it were the most natural thing in the world, with a face completely empty of expression, aimed his gun at me and fired.

Well, how odd. Blanks? It never occurred to me that it might be a prank of some sort and, of course, it wasn't. Men like that don't pull pranks. There was no anger in his eyes, no hatred. Only a matter-of-factness in his demeanour that said, I am doing this now. It's just what needs to happen. Destiny. Yours and mine. In retrospect, (which is a strange thing to say when you're dead), it was the blank expression of a radical. Neither in this world nor fully in that other. A non-person of sorts. I should have known—or maybe I did—that it wasn't money they were after.

I was on my knees before I could fully comprehend what had happened and fell numbly onto my side. When I looked down there was a small hole in the middle of my chest. I remember how neat it looked. Far too perfect a circle to be real. I placed a hand next to it, on the pec I'd been admiring in the mirror just moments ago. Why couldn't I feel anything? How was I still breathing? Was I breathing? I was faintly aware of activity around me, of slippers slapping the floor and trainers squeaking on it, and of voices that were distant echoes. I thought of my mother waiting in her car in the parking lot, but she was twenty years younger and it was my old school's car park. Then I was under water. I had to be. I'm familiar enough with the sensation. The water was warm against me and tight. Incredibly tight. I could see nothing and could only hear a sharp clicking, like that of a dolphin. I expected any moment to wake from this absurd dream. Any second now. How could any of it be real?

In Loving Memory

PLEASE JOIN US AS WE CELEBRATE (OF A PRE-TRANSITION SELF)

(NOT EXACTLY) *the life of* (OR DEATH)

[INSERT DEADNAME HERE]

(IT COULD HAVE BEEN FAR WORSE, AS THESE THINGS GO, IT'S A LOT BETTER NOW THOUGH.)

The service will take place

~~on the 23rd of June 2018,~~

~~at the Perrine Deplanade,~~

~~7 Paradise 7 Airport,~~

~~6 Fulton Scuffhaven, chin Tennee.~~

(ON THAT MID-MORNING GROCERY TRIP IN DUNDEE WHEN I CAME OUT AS NON-BINARY.) IN LATE JUNE 2020,

(I HOPE YOU LIKE PUNK, METAL, GRUNGE AND ALT, OH, AND A FAIR BIT OF INDIE. I'M ALL ABOUT IT...)

(CAKE AND KARAOKE!) *Refreshments and divertissements will be provided after the ceremony.*

Please bring ~~flowers, ribbons and written notes~~ ~~for the burial.~~

(HAMMERS, CHISELS AND NON-TOXIC PAINTS TO REDECORATE THE NAME AND TITLES ON THE GRAVESTONE.)

(I PLAN ON GETTING CREMATED IN THE END ANYWAY, I DON'T WANT TO BE SOME DEAD SLAB OF ROCK GOUGED WITH TERMS LIKE "MR." OR "HE." NO, I WANT MY ASHES TO HELP GROW A TREE.)

Just be present, no need to RSVP.

(IF YOU CAN'T MAKE IT, THERE'S ALWAYS THE NEXT CEREMONY.)

by Liam Wright

Roll/Role
by Liam Wright

Night-blue sequins
tumbling over their own dirt paths
to set suns.

Sisyphi born neatly
out of place,
above Hell, in Earth.

Quartzes escaping
their circle cells of time to move, and heave, and love, and sink in
constraints
they make themselves.

They live by fate
like flight catches gravity;
they reach up and out,
pushing, pulling, moulding futures
into their own.

Endlessly held,

carefully upright
(eggs (inside) eggs)
in near-perfect spheres.
Cyclically pregnant;

Beetles with their boulders,
boulders with their beetles.

DROWNING OF NARCISSUS

After the painting Narcissus by Caravaggio (1597-1599)
by Asbah Shah

Midnight approaches. A maddening hunger quivers the earth under a starless sky. One man is summoned by the rivers, greets the inky mirror with a sneer—quite near is his nose as it dips lower towards the surface of the lake, flirting with a reflection envied by many. Look now! A deadly fixation. There is a familiarity to how this tale will end, though the man does not know it yet. A desperation calls to him, and with greedy eyes, a face looms over the dark waters, longing to kiss an image lusted after by the masses. And so, the heavens grant him his wish. The moon winks overhead, and while he is engrossed in passion, watching his portrait in wonder between the whirl of calm waves, the ripples start a secret dance of their own. The pond beckons him forward, testing his immodesty with a sinister game of vanity; locked arms, hair sprawled, head tilted in a self-regarding loop of love.

Drip-drop.
A second passes
before the waters
capture the vain.

No one hears his struggle

as his fingers slip, splitting

themselves against the cobblestoned

lip of the pond. No one hears his plea to the gods, see,

as his fear-stricken eyes call to the sky,

wishing for a moment more with the cursed mirror.

Splashes conclude their performance,

their sounds ceasing with the night—then finally…

Narcissus drowns in his own picture.

These are excerpts from a work in progress titled "In Memory of Certain Dark Things," an anthology of clippings centered around the psychological nature of the disturbed mind.

THE CHILDREN'S CONFESSION
by Asbah Shah

in theory, you were a conjured creature from our sketchbooks, a youthful fabrication in our fearful reveries. a tentative playmate, crafted by innocent hands, formed by small paper cuts and spilt milk. childish concerns, yes, but these apprehensions shaped your growing pulse. we hadn't known about your fragile lifeline until we tasted your vengeance later on. after unearthing that our sin was indeed a sin. you lived in many places around the house: the closets, the toy chests, the bathroom cabinets. mother asked if you were a princess. father insisted you were a cowboy. we knew that you were neither. at birthday parties, you sat at the end of the table with a wicked grin. you never touched your slice of cake, you told us it was because monsters couldn't eat sweet things. we opted for a plate of lemons, but you didn't favor them either. at the park, you sank under the sandpit for hours. when the naughty kids teased us, you tugged at their legs, burying them beneath the sand until they ran out of breath. after supper, before nightfall, you gave us your warnings. we weren't to forget you. we remembered our pledges, though our hearts wavered at times. your lullabies and bedtime stories told of murderous children, of playhouses without rules. that's when you gave us the knife and said: they deserve it. we noticed you snickering in the corner as we hacked away at our parents. you promised us their blood would taste like melted cherry ice cream. it didn't.

Covenant

by Alex Deddeh

Yemmah "Mother"

My husband did not celebrate when Layla was born. If a woman births a boy, the whole village knows within the hour. It took Ibrahim three days to mumble to his brother that we had a girl. As the years passed, he grew more and more desperate for sons. Envy crawled up like a spider and bit him, spreading the venom through his heart and into his head. When our first boy came out stillborn, Ibrahim stopped coming to Church. He refused to visit his son's grave, even when I told him of the miracle. The Church cemetery is on dry, difficult land. Even digging an infant's grave proves a difficult task. But one morning, I discovered, from the place we buried our son, a pomegranate tree had begun to grow. Layla used to pick the fruit so gently. She never knew her brother, but she understood the pomegranates were a gift to her from him. From God. Despite my prayers, I miscarried again after she turned fourteen. That was when Ibrahim began talking in his sleep. He kept me up so much I started going to bed in Layla's room. I wish I had stayed and listened to the words I dismissed as nonsense. God taught me too late that sleep brings us to dangerous realms, places where the devil can come to tempt or torment. Ibrahim did not look shocked when I told him I was pregnant. It was as if he knew it would happen. Nine months later, I gave birth to a healthy, screaming son. Ibrahim named him Fuad, meaning "heart". Fitting, since the love my husband felt for him was greater than any love he had ever shown Layla. I thank God she did not inherit Ibrahim's jealousy. Layla would read Fuad stories or make up her own to see him smile. I thought Ibrahim would finally show warmth to her, if not as a daughter but as a sister to Fuad. Every day, I ask God to forgive me for such foolishness.

When Fuad turned three years old, Ibrahim told me what he had done. Our son's birth was not the miracle we all thought it to be. In exchange for Fuad, Ibrahim had promised Layla. Now Satan expected him to provide his side of the bargain. I grabbed Ibrahim's shoulders and shook him. "You pig! You coward!" I screamed, "You would not even put up your own soul!"

My husband stared at me with the stare of a stone man, a dead man. I fell to his feet and begged. "Please, don't make her his bride.There are boys in the village ready to marry her. Let Layla live and give you grandsons." Ibrahim slowly shook his head.

"Fuad will carry on my name," he said, "Her sons would not." I sobbed, pounding my fist on the floor of our house. Ibrahim spoke above my cries, "Bring me a garment with her menstrual blood."

"I will not!" I shouted. My husband dug his fingernails into my flesh and yanked me from the floor.

"Do it, woman," he growled, "Or I will go into the girl's room and take one myself." He threw me to the floor.

Our children slept soundly as I wept at the bottom of the pomegranate tree, praying to God for guidance. A ripe fruit dropped down from the branch. I held it in my hand like it was my own heart. While Ibrahim snored in his room, I snuck into the kitchen. Layla's cat, Mirza, watched me from his spot on the windowpane. Even he knew the importance of our silence that night. A mouse dashed across the floor. Mirza caught and killed it before either of us could shriek. I held my breath and carefully cut the pomegranate. I took one half in my hand and squeezed, letting its juices stain a pair of Layla's underwear. The other I hid so my husband would not suspect what I had done. I thank God that Ibrahim did not see the deception in my eyes when I handed him the cloth. That cloth was more precious to him than the daughter sleeping inches from his feet. After he left, I woke Layla and told her to take Fuad to the Church. Silently, I followed my husband on his walk to the Karun River. I hid behind the boats and watched him lay our daughter's underwear on the shore. The sand around it began to shake. A battalion of brown spiders scurried out onto the cloth, forming a hairy, throbbing mass. They burrowed their bodies into it until it disappeared under the sand. I shut my eyes and prayed. We know Farsi, we learn Arabic to survive, but our masses, our prayers, are always in Aramaic. I heard a body hit the water. I opened my eyes and saw my husband dead on the bank, a spider stuck in his heel.

*

I stood with Ibrahim's mother and sisters at the funeral. They screamed so loud that all of Ahwaz must have stopped to cover their ears. The only tears that fell from my eyes were out of rage. Rage at Ibrahim for making this terrible covenant. Rage at myself for not stopping him before it had been done. After Ibrahim was buried, I made arrangements for Fuad to live with my family in Baghdad. As much as it hurt my heart, I trusted that God would provide for him better there. I knew Layla would have to help draft the letters since I cannot read or write. But I was reluctant to ask for her assistance. This was at the beginning of her nightmares, when we still had no way to combat them. Layla looked at me, the bruises on her lips and around her eye slowly shrinking from her skin, until the next night.

"Please Mama," she said, "I need something to keep me awake."

We worked together in the kitchen, Fuad on my lap, Mirza on hers. Ibrahim's sisters visited, sipping tea and gossiping. Rumors fly out of the mouths of Chaldean women faster than steam from a boiling samwar. Badiha, the oldest, still claims I have pledged myself to Satan. She says I burned Ibrahim's things as an offering, the great stupid cow. I should have grabbed her fat face then and showed her how everything my husband owned became infested with spiders. I confess that, once, I ignored God's teaching and struck Badiha across the face. She came to my home the day after my brothers took Fuad to Baghdad. I had stayed awake all night at Layla's side, singing hymns for her, calming her as her body clenched and writhed. The morning I spent holding Fuad's blanket, my tears wetting the cloth. Badiha waddled up to my doorway and told me to wake Layla, write to my family immediately and allow Fuad to live with them. "You made my brother suffer," she spat, "I will not let you do them same to his-"

I am sure my hand stung more than Badiha's flabby jowl. It is wrong to hate her, so I pray. I pray her daughters never suffer the way mine has. I pray she never feels the pain of knowing which tree marks her baby's grave. I pray she never has to admit she cannot take care of all of her children, and survive. I lie next to Layla as she reads. She tells me my singing helps keep Satan from her sleep. I kiss her and thank God for this news. I thank Him for taking my daughter in his arms. I thank Him for giving us hope.

Bratha "Daughter"

Mirza sits on my bed, cleaning his fur while I read. Mama offered to stay up again tonight and sing. "At least let me help keep the candles lit," she said. Blessed candles, our newest discovery in our fight against Satan. Out of the corner of my eye I see Mirza stalking to the edge of the bed. He pounces on a spider and tears off its head. I smile and gently scratch the ears of my gray guardian angel. Mirza does his best to catch them all, but sometimes one manages to race past his paws and reach me. I thought I would die the first time I endured Satan's spiders' bites. But once the pain subsided, I realized it would be foolish for him to kill me. Mama stopped me from joining him in death, so he ensures that I suffer in life. His spiders seek me out when I'm awake, but when I fall asleep, he arrives, subjecting me to his rage. He hates that he can never fully claim what was promised to him by the snake. Mama does not object to me calling my father by this name. It is because of him that I live with the Devil's noose around my neck, dangling but not dying. I blame him in front of her, but in private, I blame God. If he made the pomegranate tree that sprouted from my brother's grave, if he grew the fruit that tricked the snake at the river, why does he not intervene to stop my suffering? I only say this to the cat and the candles. It would upset Mama too much to hear. Loss has wrapped so many barbs around her heart. It cannot beat without pain. All she has is me, and her faith. I irrigate her hope, pretending to find new solutions in the books she cannot read. I tell her stories about my husband falling to his knees, subdued by the sound of her song.

"His back arched when he tried to touch me," I say, "he is no match for your Aramaic, Mama."

She kisses me and thanks God for granting her this gift. There are greater sins than lying. In truth, there is no defense against Satan. I showed Mama the bruises on my face after the first night. She does not know I made sure to wait until the ones between my thighs and buttocks disappeared first.

Mama comes home with a basket of pomegranates from my brother's tree. Ever since she slapped Aunt Badiha, she's been in a better mood. I wait until Mama leaves to choke down the fresh seeds. Satan knows she believes the fruit is good for my health, so he made his lips taste like pomegranate. He knows she used to soothe my brother with jasmine, so the smell reeks from every pore of his skin when he claws his way on top of me. Mama says we have a letter from Fuad. She lies down next to me as I read it to her. He talks about the treats his aunties spoil him with, the girls he and his cousins want to marry. I remember talking with my cousins about which boys we thought would become our husbands. We used to peek across the Church at them, hoping they were peeking at us. Now, I can only look at a man for so long before his face begins to twist and morph into my husband's face, Satan's face. If Fuad ever comes back to Ahwaz, I know even he, my baby brother, will transform in this way. "God will take you straight to heaven", Mama says, stroking my hair, "He will make you a saint. I am sure of it." I nod, staring at the spider planted on the ceiling. "Whatever you wish, Layla," she says as I start to fall asleep, "He will provide."

This excerpt is part of a longer story told from the perspectives of three women living in Ahwaz, Iran.

A Game of Cricket
by Medha Singh

The fear of death is not the fear of death
but of a certain loss of pleasure / a certain threat
to the page. Pause.
Breathe. Fall through August rain. Age.

Whispers - whispers echoing in the deep, marrowless halls of
        this skeleton.
Whispers ushering current through narrow alleyways
stirring whistles advance & violet shadows
rush within the hollow bones of macilent boys thronging
with the great slap of palm against palm and *thwack*
of leather ball against hard bat.
                              Torrents: a heatwave
upon another, breaking against the unrelenting resolve
of young men pregnant with dreams of supereminence. Noble,
preternaturally masculine, rippling spirits as flags on high.
Shoulders with bones, chests with bones, the hollows of their
        eyes.
They've stretched the afternoons
of my years long.

No one ever seems to win the match.

She Had a Small Dog
by Daphne Lecoeur

I have never done a testimony before. I was simply told to write everything down. 'Put in all the details, don't miss a thing,' an officer said. So, I'm going to tell it all as it comes to me, if that's okay.

If I was to believe the darkness through the window, it must have been after 10pm. I had finished filling the bathtub, and I submerged myself in it. One disadvantage of shared bathrooms was that I always had this absurd fear of being caught naked. It was absurd, because I was the only one occupying one of the maid's rooms—oh, I forgot to mention first, I lived on the sixth floor of the building. I sank into the foam and hot water, and could hear the hubbub of the street in the distance blending with the hum of the furnace pipes. There was something relaxing about the sound of the heating. I gradually felt my muscles relax, and I began to doze off—I had a hectic day of law grad exams, you see. No more people I had to see or speak to, only me, in a safe space, with my thoughts....

But I knew it wouldn't last long. And indeed, soon, there were screams from the neighbours below, and Toby too. Toby is their dog, and the reason I'm here.

Those were the owners of my room. It was a young couple, whose wife was just a little older than me, and whose husband was the son of the man who owned most of the neighbourhood block—you guessed it, Mr. Thomakos's son. We live on St. Geneviève Hill, just a few blocks from the precinct. In the hyper centre of Paris, where any flat is worth €15,000 per square foot .... That is to say, the son didn't need to work for a living. Yet, I hardly ever came across him, despite his idleness. Might I add, he never walked Toby either. It's hard to believe they even lived in the same place.

I guess a description of the guy would help: black hair,

always wearing a shirt with suit trousers but never the jacket, expensive watch, fake tan. I never saw his face. He always hid it under ridiculously large sunglasses, but I could see the carnivorous smile he had on when he would see me and that had struck me enough to make me wary. I put him in this range of poorly educated but well-born brats; child kings who have grown in body but never in mind. This is hasty judgment on my part, perhaps, but it had prevented me from getting to know him, which I was very pleased with. On the other hand, his wife, I knew her a little better. I have to say, now I kind of wish I didn't.

Like many times a week, the din of voices continued under the floor, accompanied by occasional muffled noises. The barking grew louder, more helpless, its vibrations making the water in my bath tremble. Completely submerged, I felt as if protected by a bubble; I heard every sound echoing through the water, and my ears. I felt isolated from everything, and omniscient at the same time.Maybe this, at that moment and not before, is why I dared to get involved in their business.

The arguments I heard had started a few months before, shortly after the woman had moved in. She arrived soon after I did. Taking advantage of the indolence of my summer holiday, she had asked me to help her set up her few things, and I wasn'tquick-witted enough to work up an excuse. I remember I was surprised to see almost nothing but clothes and makeup inside her luggage. No books, no family pictures, nothing that seemed personal. It seemed like she would only be there for a short stay. She seemed delighted with my assistance. I was probably the first to show her any resemblance of affability in the neighbourhood. Oh yes, and the woman was 25 years old tops: white, petite, very coquettish, with auburn hair and hazel eyes. I felt a weird vibe coming from her though, like we were on totally different frequencies. However, she had brought a small dog, and I preferred her over the guy only for that.

You see, I don't even know the names of the people in the building, I never bothered to learn them. But, small Toby is definitely my favourite, by a long shot. I just feel that dogs should be rewarded for not being people, and what a dog he was. A nice dachshund, adorable and full of energy, who doesn't seem to fit in with his very preppy mistress whom I've never really seen smile. Toby always barked at his owners, but I never heard him do it to me. I would see him a few times a week, and he was the only living thing I would gladly talk to, except my mother on the phone, once a month.

There have been several times when the woman opened the door to her flat and waved at me, as I was walking down the stairs from the sixth to the fifth floor. She would ask me to walk her dog for an hour or two. In exchange, she would give me euro bills I rarely ever saw as a student—50, 100, 200. Little did she know I would have walked Toby for free anytime, but why would I tell her that when I could afford eating at a restaurant instead of cup noodles? She never got more than her head out of the gap of the door, like she was hiding something on her body. It was the only thing out of the ordinary that we exchanged. I could have tried to strike up a real conversation a few times, that is true, but first of all, I didn't care much about making bonds with strangers in the building. Plus, there was always something in her voice, her posture and especially her look that I couldn't describe…. It made me feel extremely uncomfortable. No doubt hearing these operas of screams accompanied by barking almost every night exhausted me. So I avoided talking to her too much. I had felt like a coward, yet I would risk my flat trying to meddle anyhow.

And suddenly, the voices became even louder—no, actually they were louder than they had ever been before. My water bubbles shook like waves crashing against the sides of the tub, while the shouting of insults and the various clashes began to crescendo. Toby barked and yelped louder and louder, relentlessly, like asking for help. Falling, smashing, increasingly violent sounds could be heard in the commotion. But the only clear thing in my mind was Toby's barking, and my heart beating wildly in my ears. What should I have done at that moment?

The male voice suddenly seemed to explode. Should I call the police?

There was a loud thud, a muffled woman's scream. Who else could I call for help?

That's when I got out of the bath. I dried myself off, dressed in a panic, stormed out into the corridor, jumped down four steps at a time until I reached the ground floor. I ran to get to the police station two blocks away, and here I am now.

Because the barking had stopped.

Just Past the Middle of Nowhere

by Andrew Mackenzie

00:04

Four minutes past midnight, just past the middle of nowhere. The night enveloped them completely, welcomed them gladly and swallowed them whole. The freeway stretched ahead. A pair of yellow lines leading him on and on and on. There was nothing, except for him and his car with his girlfriend snoring gently in the passenger seat. Driving in silence to avoid waking her, there was nothing to focus his mind. It wandered aimlessly into the void outside the windows and to the stars.

He had never seen so many. Millions and millions of tiny pinpricks of light so many miles away yet keeping him company on this seemingly endless drive. He wondered what was out there, in the endless plain of still black night between himself and the star-spangled sky.

Coyotes.

Did they have Coyotes in New Mexico? He thought that they probably would, given its mountainy-deserty-ness. There was probably a word for that, but he liked his description better. It made sense that there would be coyotes out here. Maybe he'd read it somewhere? In a guidebook or something. He knew they had snakes here, and roadrunners—which he had discovered with disappointment—did not go *meep meep*.

Snakes and Coyotes.

His hands gripped the wheel a little bit tighter, and his ears kept twitching at all the little sounds that cars make. Did that rattle mean the engine was about to blow a piston? What was that bump?

The last thing he wanted was to be stranded in the middle of nowhere, surrounded by God-knows-what in the darkness and without mobile reception. Snakes and Coyotes. Vultures too.

Probably.

The freeway stretched on and on in the darkness.

00:34

How hadn't he noticed half an hour slipping by? That wasn't good. Any more of that, and he'd fall asleep at the wheel. If that happened and the inevitable crash didn't kill him, then his girlfriend almost certainly would.

They'd never find his body either. She could drag him into the desert and leave him for the Snakes and the Coyotes.

He'd be nothing but bones by next Thursday.

They'd driven to New Orleans a few days ago to meet his girlfriend's family. For the return leg, they had decided to follow route 66 for a more scenic journey, and because neither had driven it before and didn't know when they would get the chance again. They had talked about flying but had ultimately decided that driving would be better.

He chuckled to himself.

Scenic journey. He gazed out of the window at the vast expanse, stretching to the horizon where the darkness of the desert melted into the sky shimmering with shining stars. It was scenic, he supposed, in its own way.

He tapped his fingers on the wheel, and casually turned his attention back to the road. The problem with American roads was that they were all arrow-straight. No capacity for surprises.

Something broke the darkness in front of him, illuminated in brilliant white light. Something big. Something in the middle of the road. Too close and hurtling towards him. Too close. Too fast. He jerked the wheel in a desperate effort to avoid whatever it was. It flashed past his window. It was person-sized and dressed in white. He lost control, the tyres lost grip and the car spun down the freeway. He hung on grimly.

His girlfriend woke up screaming, joining the screeching tyres in a tortured symphony. The sound and the spinning deafened his senses, disorientated his mind. He closed his eyes, let go of the wheel and hoped that they didn't hit anything too hard.

Eventually, the car came to a stop.

Smoke rose from the tyres where they had burned across the freeway. Steam rose from the tortured engine, thin wisps of smoke, twisting and turning like ghostly dancers.

Shaking, he turned to her, and she stared back at him with eyes wide and chest rising and falling rapidly. Adrenaline pumped, slowing time to a crawl, and he watched as the fear on her face turned to confusion, turned to anger.

Then she punched him, hard.

And time returned to normal.

"What the fuck was that?" she yelled. "If you fell asleep, I swear to God I—"

"I think I hit someone."

00:43

Tick Tick…Tick Tick…Tick Tick…Tick Tick…Tick Tick….

The sound of the hazard lights cut through the silence.

They looked at one another.

Tick Tick…Tick Tick…Tick Tick…Tick Tick…Tick Tick….

Their minds struggled to reconcile with reality.

He looked out of the window and back down the freeway. The car had come to a stop diagonally across the freeway. He stared out of the passenger widow into the darkness. It was impossible to see more than a few metres.

"We can't leave," he said after minutes or hours, he didn't really know.

They could. Nobody would know. Nobody would find whatever, whoever, was out there until much, much later, driving along the freeway in the bright light of the early morning, discovering a figure crumpled and broken at the side of the road. But it was wrong. The thought of someone lying on the asphalt just out of the beam of his headlights was too much to bear.

His mind was racing. Snakes and Coyotes.

He climbed out of the car, knowing that if he hesitated for even a moment, he would stop himself.

The smell of burnt rubber hit him. In the morning, drivers would all see the tyre marks and wonder what had transpired.

The door slammed shut behind him, the jolt seemed to reawaken his senses. It was cold, but that wasn't what was making him shiver. The area around him was lit up in the orange of the hazard lights pulsating in the darkness in a beat with his heart. He looked around and saw his girlfriend climbing out of the car.

"There's no one there," she said.

"I just want to check."

Something was telling him that there was someone there, just out of the light.

Lying in the darkness, where the Snakes and the Coyotes roamed. "Stay with the car."

He took his first tentative steps, keeping to the side of the road. It almost seemed ridiculous, nobody else was around and yet here he was. Amazing how habit takes over, all those times he'd been pulled to the side of the road by anxious parents. As he walked, his shadows reached forwards into the void and disappeared, greedily consumed by the darkness. He didn't call out. Somehow, he was too scared to do so. Terrified of what might answer back.

Pulling out his phone, he turned on the torch and kept going. It did nothing, except make the darkness outside its beam seem darker still. His muscles tensed, he could almost feel their fibres vibrating under his skin. His mind raced ahead of him, trying to predict what was awaiting him in the dark. A body lying by the side of the road, tyre marks over it. Almost cartoonish. He couldn't shake off the absurdity of his imagination. They had spun further than he had expected. Looking over his shoulder, the car seemed so far away. He kept going.

Then, in the darkness, he saw something. Someone. A girl.

Dressed in white. He wondered if 'dressed' was the right word. After all, she was wearing only a thin white vest and a pair of white boxers. She was covered in bright red blood, which glistened on her black skin.

She wasn't lying on the asphalt. Rather she was sitting on the side of the road. He exhaled a great wave of relief. He hadn't hit her then. She was shaking. From shock, or from the cold, either seemed plausible. She *had* just nearly been hit by a car. She didn't acknowledge him at first.

"Hello?" he said.

Hello. Really? he thought to himself.

Nothing. As though she didn't hear. Or didn't process.

She just stared.

"Shit," he muttered to himself.

He took a step forward, and his phone torch washed over her again. Now he was closer, he could see the extent of her injuries.

Her face was bruised, lips swollen and bleeding. Her thick, curly hair was matted with dirt. Her arms were cut to shreds, deep gashes from which blood still seeped. It was the same story with her legs. Her clothes were dirty and blackened. Stained with blood. It had pooled between her legs. He found himself staring, staring for a moment too long. Long enough for his brain to work it out.

"Help me," she said quietly.

01:03

They carried her to the car. His girlfriend gave her some clothes. They dug around under the seats and found a nearly empty water bottle. The girl drank the dregs gratefully. Nobody said a word.

The only noise was the rumbling of the wheels over the asphalt. The darkness that had felt so far away now pressed against the windows, enveloping them, suffocating them. The stars had gone. Replaced by something inexplicable but far more oppressive. Understanding.

He drove on, searching for the safety of neon lights. He drove on until the lights of a gas station lit up the darkness.

01:37

The attendant called the police as soon as they arrived.

The gas station was in the middle of nothingness. A neon oasis in the black desert.

A State Trooper arrived first. He spotted the car from its headlights on the horizon, still a great distance away. Two pinpricks that could have been stars, flickering as he rode the bumps of the road.

"Hellavanight," was the first thing he said. He had kind eyes.

Casual. Almost flippant, he thought. But strangely apt. What else was there to say?

He had questions. They answered them honestly, and as fully as they could. He thanked them for their intervention. "Were lucky you guys being out there. Lord knows what else could a found her first. Coyotes, for one."

Despite everything, the words *Knew it*, formed in his head.

"A detective will be here soon, will want to talk to you. You understand, right?"

They understood.

The paramedics arrived first. They ushered her into the back of an ambulance. Wrapped her in a blanket and gave her shots. Took blood. Gave her painkillers. His girlfriend stayed with the girl. She had always been a comforting presence. He sat in the car, staring at the clock on the dash.

02:17

The detective arrived in one of those chunky, oversized, black and white cop cruisers with the huge lights on the roof and the intimidating bars in the front. They always looked like they were compensating for something. Intimidation rather than protection. He stepped out of the car wearing mirrored sunglasses.

In the middle of the night.

"Right, let's get this over with," he said. "My colleague says you picked the gal up on the side of the road," he drawled, "care to tell me what happened, and we can all be on our way?"

"She was out in the middle of nowhere, and we nearly hit her with the car. She seemed scared and hurt. We picked her up and we saw that she needed help. She will get help, won't she? You'll find whoever did this to her."

"Can anyone corroborate your story?"

"I'm sorry?"

The cop yawned again. "Anyone else see the girl on the road?"

"Not that I know of."

"I see." He made a couple of notes in his notebook. He flipped it shut.

"You see anyone else out there on the road?"

"No," he said, slowly, "We didn't see another car for hours."

"So you can't back up her story then."

"How else do you think she got out there?"

"Maybe she went for a walk."

"The nearest town is fifteen miles away. You're telling me that the idea she got up and went for a walk through the desert in the middle of the night in just her underwear is more believable than her own testament?"

The cop leaned forward. "Why d'you care so much? Huh? You seem pretty keen for me to swallow this story of yours. Maybe there was no one else out there. Maybe a young couple picks up a gal to spice things up. Maybe they rough her up a bit after they're done, force her to tell a different story. Ain't no witnesses to say otherwise. Now I got two versions, and I gotta pick the one I think's more plausible. What do you think?"

He can't think of a reply. Something catches the words in the back of his throat and smothers them.

"I thought as much," said the cop, "thanks for your time."

He sauntered lazily back to his cruiser.

The State Trooper took their details, said they might hear

from them again and said they were free to go. Said all the right things. "We'll do what we can" and all that. And that was that. It was over.

03:04

At four minutes past three, they left the gas station, just past the middle of nowhere.

The Big Dipper
by Olivia Thomakos

Show us your kitchen in the sky,
ignorant boys laugh at my astronomy.

Stargazing in the corn field
that didn't belong to any of us,

they couldn't grasp Alkaid, Mizar or Alioth –
couldn't swallow Megrez, Phecda, Dubhe or Merak.

Next you'll point out the Great Triangle or
the Big Line, they say.

I laugh with them because I'm lying
next to you. You hand me the beer we are sharing.

I'm not sure what came next,
the empty can or the Lyrid stars

but watching you trace the chasing lights
I got exactly what I wished for.

Beatha, Bás, Lobhadh
by Erin Ketteridge

Coalesce (Preamble)

What have you seen? What have you thought?

All manner of things. I bet you've seen innumerable tragedies and disasters, right on the cusp of becoming. I bet you don't even realise how close you've been to life-altering moments, life-altering people. All those different possibilities, all those different paths and levels you could have followed. Who and where would you be? Would you be better? Would you love more or less?

What would you see? Let's think. The leaves of the trees gently shimmering, burnt gold sunlight filtering through the glass frames. Especially for you. From a chair at a table in a function room surrounded by solemn looking friends and filled with half-eaten sandwiches, you feel as though you could open the window and step out onto the air, and that no one would see you leave. There are birds scudding about outside, so many birds, twittering and fluttering. At some point you must have picked up your drink and moved over to the window, because you find yourself with your nose pressed against the glass like you did as a child in front of the washing machine, trying to see every feather, trying to identify every species. Your mind spins and spins and spins. You're thinking about how odd a funeral feels without a burial. You're wondering when you will feel like you've really said goodbye.

Goodbye is nothing but a cycle. Hello-goodbye-hello-goodbye-hello. Flicker of rabbit tails scampering in primal fear. You're being buried alive but you're eating the dirt too fast. Fat little worms are stretching out their fingers to tickle your spinal cord. You'll wake when the rain comes, when it dribbles down through the layers of earth and rubble and revives your skin. You'll remember everything, briefly, before you surface again as someone new in a brand-new body. It's scarred, it's painted by someone who is too scared to skin an animal. The pummels of grief feel like an invitation to brawl. For the rest of your life you will feel the need to revel in violence but never understand why. The cycle begins again, a washing machine of colour. *Red and blue and purple and pink and white and all the colours you've ever felt.* A head full of colours until the shell splits open and reveals all you've worked for. Your mind, that shining, dirty beacon, any and all thoughts you've ever had are set free. A little iridescent seed, a little oyster pearl. Bring it to the ocean. Bring it to me.

Get down to the beach, get to walking in the muddy rivulets, before the tears start to fall. Don't worry, I'll look after you. In the meantime, do whatever makes you feel good. Do what gives you the tingle in your fingertips. Walk sand and city and mountain. Hike and bike and read and bake. Laugh and kiss with open mouths, be joyful and always kind. People deserve kindness, even when they don't. You can be that person. I know you can.

Scrub and grub and scrub and grub. Eat and clean and sleep. A tidy mind is a tidy house and the same inside out. You have been offered a spectacle. You are welcome to bear witness. It would be my pleasure to add it to the washing machine. Red blue purple pink white orange green and the nothingness of heartbreak. Reach out. Taste. Tastes of nothing, but smells of whatever you miss most, and something you forgot about a long time ago. Don't try to touch it. It isn't there.

Don't worry though, I'll look after it for you.

Life-death-life-death-life-death. And so on. And so forth.

Preamble. Amble. Coalesce.

Begin With the Feet

Somewhere in the back fields, Andrew can remember his father telling him to begin with the feet. He would string the body from a branch and hand the boy a sharp knife.

'Begin with the feet,' he'd say. 'Then the rest comes easy.'

Andrew could do it when he was little, when he was still brave. Cutting off the feet was no problem—it was like slicing carrots. The bones were so thin, sometimes you wouldn't even know it was happening until the limbs fell off. But as he started to get older, he started to understand. When he began with the feet he could picture the burrows and the warrens, the infants waiting for their parents to return. He could see the flashes of tails as the creatures fled in primal panic from the footsteps of his father. When he began with the feet, he could only look in the eyes where dead, still fear lingered.

Once, whilst mouthing a silent prayer of apology into the dark, vacant depths, the knife slid through the tendons of the leg much faster than usual and slashed his palm. He thinks that was when his father realised he couldn't do it, even with his hoarse, hopeful—

'Keep your eye on it.'

His father took his bloodied hand and wiped at it with his dirty handkerchief, kissing his son's cheek as he did so to hide the tears. He sent him back up the fields to the warm kitchen and sweet tea and finished the rabbits himself. Deft artist, like wielding a brush. He asked for John's help the next day, and Andrew had never seen so pure a look of delight on his younger brother's face. The knife was firm in his hand, firmer than it had ever been in his own.

Portrait

Makes me nervous, how he watches *me*.

Hillside. Wind is around us, and if I were with someone else I would feel powerful. Would feel the rumble around me and the thunder beneath the ground and know that the earth calls for me. I would know that it responds to my feet on its grass, that the hills stretch and roll before me, reclining into the blue-tinged pink of the sky, only to be viewed by my eyes. The artist wants to capture this power, I know—he has observed the way that the world stops and submits to a twitch of my eye, yet with him watching me I feel that even if I signalled with all my motion, the world would continue to slouch past.

The hillside is cold, and the wind is with us. Winds through my hair, pulls my hands, touches my legs, fills my dress. This dress is too thin for the weather, but the swell of warmth from the parcel I hold to my mouth warms my lips, serves as a tonic against the chill of the artist's glare. The smell of the bread wrapped in fabric is a friend's warm hand pressed against my cheek, a moment's silence.

Somewhere on the next hill over, someone is whistling and shouting commands to a dog. From the urgency of the shepherd's voice, I picture papers blowing everywhere. Neat piles whisked into large swirls of chaos. I hope for him and the dog and the sheep that the wind dies down soon, so its vague howls will no longer clog the pup's ears and send it flailing down the wrong side of the flock.

Wonder if the artist is thinking this, whether he is too busy studying the pause above my brows or crease in my left cheek, or the scar that joins my forehead and my hairline. Wonder what he thinks of the scar. When I was younger, it bothered me. Wondered whether the pink and silver gash made people's stomach's flip, wonder why it was there, what terrible story shadowed me. Wondered whether people thought that the moon which hung on my face held me apart, rendered me vacant in some mystical physical way, such is the way my mountain people think. But then I remember the artist's hands. His shirt too thin, like mine, a board clutched in a dirty hand and a paint swatch branded in his other, scarred, fingers.

Wonder quietly whether his scars bother him, whether people have made the same assumptions. But I can see the strength in the grip of his maimed hand, can feel the power we both share in knowing that at least some part of us was saved.

Maybe this is why it makes me nervous when he watches. The fear that he is the same, and hears my thoughts privately as I do.

Earthside

Going Earthside today. Heard the scratch sometime in the last year. The roots of the largest tree above have relayed a message from their hairy touch, they've stretched far enough into the gloom of my resting place, stroked my arms apart from their folded embrace, lured my fingers away from my aching chest and wiggled their feelers into my ears to prod awake my brain.

They scratched and scratched and scratched until my eyes were open, and then they could say, 'the worms have told me something'. I asked the roots what the worms had told them. They said, 'two people have been forgotten. The worms have had their fill. The Earthside creatures have lost their interest. Now it's *your turn* to go Earthside and see if they want to come in'. I opened my mouth wider to yawn, wakened, melted from atrophy, and let the soil in. I crunched it in my teeth for my breakfast and asked the roots to stop scratching at my brain. I wiggled my toes, and I started the slow journey up. I paused along the way and introduced myself again to the people I brought down from Earthside years ago. I reintroduce myself because often the creatures forget where they are and sometimes still think they're Earthside, and they're surprised when they turn their empty eye sockets and moaning mouths towards me and find my little gruesome face there.

I remind them where they are and that they were forgotten Earthside, and that makes them moan louder. It tends to distress them. Others remember me. They twitch a finger in hello-and-thanks and watch me struggle on. Depths and depths and depths. Earthside creatures would think the soil like an Ocean. Like water, rivers, and tides, bloody and raw, rush in rush out, pound and beat, crushing and whipping and crying with white hands. Except the soil yields, obeys when you push it apart, and water doesn't, water rushes in and fills everything, it's obnoxious. Water is everywhere Earthside, that's why they don't call me too often.

After I rested for a while, made the last push. Going Earthside today. Reaching the last few miles now, and then, without warning, I pop straight up. Water everywhere, water in the air up here, and sunlight too. Been lost to sunlight for some time now, feels good to be warm again. I bask and gasp for a minute. Lay and stretch myself out. Everything is big and green and wet far as the eye can see. The grass presses against my back, eager tips try to taste. 'Food?' they ask, 'Food? Food?'

'No,' I say, 'Not me, the power within me is beyond anything your soul can take. A taste of me is to taste decay.' The grass retreats.

I begin my crawl. Got to find the forgotten. They must be round here somewhere, can smell them.

Creep up two pairs of feet, toes rotted at the ends and legs bitten and bruised. Yes, Earthside creatures have had their fill. Put my own scratchers in their ears this time, tickle the gooey putrid brains awake. The man sits and through his blind mouth says, 'Hello? Hello?' The woman turns to him and says, 'Are you alright?' then she can smell it too and she knows they're not. She turns her own mute eyes to me and I take back my scratchers. 'Who are you?' she says. 'I am Below,' I tell her. 'You haven't seen me before because I don't live Earthside.'

She opens her mouth to ask, but through the gap all the marvels of God rush in instead. They've been swarming around me, waiting for the moment they could, and she gulps them down as the rest struggle up the man's collapsed nostrils. They shake a bit and then the only question the woman has for me is 'Why do you have to do it? Why do you have to take the forgotten Earthside?' I try to do something like a shrug and say, 'Someone has to keep an eye on these things.' The man doesn't take it so well. 'I had so much more I wanted to do,' he says, 'so much more we planned to see.' 'Hush, little heart,' I say. 'There is time for all, endless time, Beneath.' He nods and looks down at his grim hands as I begin to pick up their loose little bones, gathering them in my arms.

'Time to go, I say,' and they press their lips to the ground to kiss goodbye to Earthside. I take their ankles and pull them down with me. Maybe months into the crawl back down the woman asks about how long it must have taken me to get to them. 'A while,' I say. 'I got the scratch more than a year ago.' She can't nod her head anymore because her spine is too fragile, but her silence is one of assent. The man hasn't said very much in the last thirty days and is still quiet when I drop them off a little way from the largest tree's roots. I like these two, they're quiet. I'll keep them close. 'Thank you,' the woman says. The man groans with miserable gratitude. I give them back their loose little bones and head back to my own Beneath place.

I settle in, don't know how long for, don't know if to wait for the scratch or not. I close my eyes again, feel the little clumps of dirt on my arms. Feel the little pressures of creatures who have come to say welcome home. In time, even they go too.

Feels good to be home again.
Feels good to not be Earthside.

The Uninvited Guest
by Han Le

The cathedral's bell tolled a mournful song,
to lull lonesome spirits, those presences—
unseen, to rest in their dark realm. The strong

wind shrieked with incessant violence
through the cracked window, sent chilly air
into my room. The night whispered in silence.

The trees' moving shadows on the wall shared
the appearance of a woman, one who danced
with her demonic lover in a nightmare.

I returned to my book, keeping my glances
from the eerie scene. Tap! Tap! Tap! Tap!
"What the hell is that noise?" I looked askance

at the window where the tapping arose. I grabbed
a broom, approached the noise, ready to fight.
Just a startled bird flying away. I laughed

at my foolish angst, but a chill ran down my spine
when I heard a whimpering sound that tore
through the just resettled silence. Fright

engulfed me. My body froze, my core
tightened, my heartbeats hastened. A gust
rushed through me as a figure with an abhorred

face with hollow eyes and twisted smile. Disgust!
It approached me with triumph expanded
across its pale face. My courage, once robust,

shrank to nothingness; it wrapped its cold hand
round my neck. When thoughts of death pressed close,
my brain flashbacked to all past events. "Goddamned!"

Fear–gone. I flung away from its cold arms. It froze
with shock. I directed it toward the desk
where cannabis lay scattered on a poem.

I rolled two joints, and gave one to the grotesque,
placed one between my lips. We filled our lungs
with divine smoke. "Life's just a burlesque

of hallucinations! Let's have some fun
tonight," I paused and smiled to my weird mate.
It reclined on the wall and softly hummed

the chorus of a lo-fi song that I'd played
every night. I joined along, aware
that he had been here since then. "That's okay!

You are more fun than most people. Their
phony rambles, their hypocrisy just bore
the shit out of me. Yes, your presence scared

me at first. Your face must be the model for
the devil in The Exorcist," I showed
the ghost a photo of Regan, and we snorted

with laughter. "Yet I think you also know
that nothing is as scary as the hearts
of humans, unfathomable, where evils flow

in their veins and disguise in goodness. When we part
tonight, I hope you find salvation,

though I will be lonely again." I caught

his tender smile. What a lovely reaction!
Outside, the sun slowly rose to start
a new day. The friend hugged me with affection

and walked toward the heaven glow. My heart
sank while lighting another, watching him depart.

To CB15A

by Vidisha Ghosh

If you ever asked about House CB15A, they would tell you about the strange things that happened inside. Its inhabitants were seasoned creators of chaos. They deep-fried tofu, broke at least two dishes a day, left a credit card in a pile of carrots, and once placed a jackfruit the size of a chubby puppy in the middle of the dining room. No one knew where the jackfruit came from. Everyone ate, conversed, and temporarily built their lives around the mysterious fruit. Then, one day, it was gone. Made into a curry. End of story.

Strange people lived in CB15A. So strange that every time someone patted Mother and Father with a melancholy sigh, expressing concern because they had no son, they seemed oddly happy. Years ago, a Neighbourhood Nosy Bitch (NNB for further reference), upon hearing the news about the birth of their second daughter, had shrieked with grief, 'OH DEAR LORD, A GIRL AGAIN?' She covered her gaping mouth with the end of her sari, beads of post-lunch sweat gathering on her hairy upper lip. That shriek roughly translated into, 'Come on, losers. Life has given you another female offspring, and you are ecstatic? What about your inheritance? What about your influence in society?'

Now, for those wondering what an NNB is: NNBs are senior members of Well-Wishers Ltd., an ancient organisation of perpetually hypercritical creatures who resist privacy and progress. Alongside NNBs, one will find Unwarranted Commentators, Unconstructive Critics, Nitpicky Relatives, Comparers of Children's Achievements and Disgruntled Body Shamers frequenting Ltd. Company meetings.

Now that we are gossiping about CB15A, let's discuss a thing or two about Mother and Father. They were the oddest of couples. Why? For starters, theirs was a marriage of equals. YES. YOU HEARD THAT RIGHT. They were supportive, not patronising.

Affectionate, not stifling. They lived like best friends, arguing, drinking, eating, and thriving. And if that wasn't unbelievable enough, imagine everyone's horror when it was revealed that they had even dated for a while before they were married. Rebels without a cause.

In 1995, Mother and Father were Boy and Girl. They were frolicking about, earning their dough, and doing whatever the hell they wanted. Until they were discovered and had to get married because here's what they were told (this was in Bengali, so the translation is sketchy):

Others: You must marry.

Boy and Girl: …

Others: Society calls for it.

Boy and Girl: …

Others: Our relatives disapprove of such doings. Your activities traumatise them.

Boy and Girl: What activities?

Others: Unwed dalliances. Non-Marriage Certificate Approved Pursuits.

Boy and Girl: Okay. But—

Others: OKAY. YOU SAID OKAY. SO DO WE CALL FIVE HUNDRED PEOPLE, MAKE A CIRCUS OUT OF IT, AND GIVE THIS RELATIONSHIP A LABEL?

Boy and Girl: Well, we aren't entirely sure if labels are necessary.

Others: So, what do we call you? Lovers? LORD, THE SCANDAL.

Boy and Girl: What about—

Others: This conversation is over.

In 1996, Boy and Girl became Husband and Wife, and in 1997, parents to Clueless Elder Female. Now, they are called Mother and Father. Bizarre events happened around the birth of Clueless Elder Female. What should have been a dark occasion marked by despair at the birth of a girl was misconstrued by the loonies as festive cheer. Yet, Well-Wishers Ltd. were optimistic. They hoped for a second trial, crossing their fingers that the next offspring would yield the necessary outcome. But seven years later, when the Clever Younger Female arrived in the world, squealing, adorable and very much a violation of male primogeniture, Well-Wishers Ltd. were forced to abandon all hopes of a male bloodline.

They gathered themselves over samosas to realign their objectives.

NNB 1: Two daughters. What do we do now?

NNB 2: Bring out the 'All that Matters is Arranged Marriage' Module. We have to monitor the family and ensure the girls become suitable spouses.

NNB 3: We start by suggesting monthly investments in gold. And, of course, jewellery designs.

NNB 4: Organic face packs for a fairer complexion. Boyzz like a nice glow.

So, Well-Wishers Ltd. observed Mother and Father, praying they would devote their time and money into moulding Clueless Elder Female and Clever Younger Female into dolls made of 'Wife Material'. Do you know the Wife Material? The always-quiet, consistently selfless, never-doing-anything-for-themselves, sacrificial lamb fabric that sells for a pittance? Yep, that one.

But even that was a waste of time. As Well-Wishers Ltd. observed Mother and Father, they noticed controversial, MASSIVE parenting errors. The company maintained yearly records, noting everything they did wrong:

   1. Excessive Educational Spending
      Mother and Father worked extra shifts, travelled in overcrowded public transport, and never bought anything for themselves. That's the middle-class price for private schools, sponsoring college in the capital, and ensuring your daughters can survive the ever-changing world.

Note: The correct use of hard-earned money is spending on only particular assets that can be leveraged at the right time to purchase extravagant gifts for future husbands.

Recommended Literature: *Well-Wishers Ltd. Guide to Investments for Burdened Girl Parents*

2. Too Many Holidays
Mother and Father hadn't grown up with much. So, they made sure the girls never felt that way. They saved for sixteen years and took them to Sri Lanka, Switzerland, France, Spain, and Portugal. It was difficult (thank you skewed exchange rates, taxes, and privatisation of essential services). But now they have Mickey Mouse ears from Disneyland.

Note: An occasional holiday is permissible. **BUT,** it must be close to home, unstimulating, and unrelated to the mumbo-jumbo of "We want them to see the world."

Recommended Literature: *The Well-Wishers Ltd. List of 2022's Best, Most Monotonous Travel Destinations*

3. <u>ALCOHOL</u>
(THE DEVIL; ridiculous + immoral + precocious + ridiculous)

When the time was right, Mother and Father explained responsible drinking and only insisted on safety. They created no hullabaloo and stepped back, allowing their girls to understand the world for themselves. At CB15A, Saturday nights were for wine and kebabs. Christmas Eve meant Old Monk and Coke.

Note: Well-Wishers have a strict no-alcohol policy, especially at home. Proper parents foster a tense relationship with alcohol, refuse to have mature conversations about it, and force kids into drinking in secrecy.

Recommended Literature: Well-Wishers Ltd. *Top Tips for Resisting Vices and Fostering Values*

> 4. Cheering on Wild Decisions
> The girls didn't fit into a purely academic scheme. Clueless Elder Female scribbled, and Clever Younger Female loved desserts. So, Mother and Father became co-applicants for an educational loan for Creative Writing. Then, they bought baking supplies and encouraged coffee cakes and fudge experiments.

Note: Medical school, engineering, and an MBA are acceptable. But undertake all educational ventures with a clear understanding thatencouraging your daughters' passion isn't an essential priority. Instead, parents need to focus on financing a grand wedding (expenses including fodder for the groom's horse).

Recommended Literature: Well-Wishers Ltd. *Handbook of Lavish Weddings to Please Irrelevant People*

Of course, Well-Wishers Ltd. was concerned. CB15A wasn't getting it right—a certified disaster. Mother and Father were a mess, enjoying their lives and letting their daughters live theirs. The daughters were growing into independent women. And then came the batty Grandmothers. Oh Lord, the Grandmothers. Crocodilesin cotton saris. Defying every norm Well-Wishers Ltd. dictated for the elderly. According to their *2022 Guide to Being Autocratic Older Women Trying to Bring Down Other Women,* women above sixty had to follow at least some of the following rules:

- Constantly interfere in all decisions.
- Hinder progress by projecting internal grief from the injustices you have suffered onto younger women attempting to overcome them.
- Insist upon subservience. (This can be subtle, like preventing your daughter/daughter-in-law from enjoying her meal until everyone else has finished their food, or aggressive, such as treating her personal and professional achievements as the butt of sexist jokes.)
- Spend 70% of your day whining, criticising, and making life difficult for everyone. The remaining 30% is for establishing your moral superiority by repeating one statement multiple times: 'When I was young...' Get creative. For example, 'When I was young, I couldn't say a word before my husband. But look at you, all chatty, opinionated, and acting as an equal.'
- Read and quote religious literature. It's acceptable to misquote it. You are old. No one should question you.

But even the Grandmothers at CB15A were devious. They adhered to nothing. Instead, they drank countless cups of tea, forgot to convey messages, and watched soap operas for six hours a day. They were brutally honest and hated infringement of their space. So, if the clock struck five and you were milling about, they would ask you to fuck off. That's the time for tea and the deafening soap opera about the love story of a surgeon and his reincarnated lover. Honestly, the Grandmothers weren't bothered as long as the rains didn't disturb the cable network.

(Note: Well-Wishers Ltd. classified such reckless, enabling Grandmothers as Old Women Gone Rogue.)

CB15A made many lists: groceries, repairs, hospital appointments, religious occasions, and social events. They never relaxed, throwing themselves into organisation and more organisation until all that remained were tick marks, bills, and mini lists from longer lists. So, when they had to send off Clueless Elder Female, Mother and Father went into overdrive.

Coats/jackets/Gloves/Woolly socks   Waterproof shoes Teabags
~~Pressure Cooker~~
Student loan (?) New underwear (Remember to buy white/nude bras)
Masalas (Turmeric, Cumin Whole + Powder, Coriander, Asafetida)
Cosmetics- NEEDS A SEPARATE LIST
Sanitary Napkins   MEDICINES- NEEDS A SEPARATE LIST

Their chaos was timeless. Create chaos. Create lists. It rationalises the jolt of change. What is evolution but a series of To-Do Lists either faultlessly executed or horribly sidelined? Even during goodbyes, Well-Wishers Ltd. had endless faults to pinpoint. This time, Unwarranted Commentators (UC) bickered about everything.

UC 1: There's so much to do at home. Why send free labour away?
Mother: Isn't Scotland always cold? She will need a warmer coat.
UC 2: Is it safe? Leaving her out there in the world? Alcohol, Boyzz, Freedom.
Father: Done it before. Didn't care then. Don't care now. We know what she needs.
UC 3: Boundaries. Cooking lessons. Weight loss.
Father: An extra pair of glasses. Good to keep one handy.

Huffing and puffing, frustrated with the madness, the UCs stormed out of CB15A. As a sign of protest, Well-Wishers Ltd.

temporarily called off their visits. Yet their twenty-first century, state-of-the-art prying technologies always kept a close eye. They were determined to fix the unit, especially Mother and Father. Many days later, company representatives returned, joining the household for tea.

UC 1: How is school, Clever Young Female? Have you chosen your subjects?

Clever Young Female: I was thinking about Human—

UC 2: The human body? The sciences? An acceptable, part-time pursuit for women.

Clever Young Female: Oh no, but I meant Humanities.

UC 3: SSSH, we don't utter that word. That thing is for the ones who are bad at maths. It's the dark side.

The UCs turned their attention to Mother and Father.

UC 1: It must be hard without Clueless Elder Female.

Father: Ah, but she is enjo—

UC 2: And the EMIs. Bad economy for an educational loan.

Mother: It is only tempo—

NNB 1: What's the point? Our research predicts creative careers never take off.

Mother and Father: That is such nonse—

NNB 2: Don't you worry. At Well-Wishers Ltd., we believe that every mistake is a learning opportunity. So be careful about Clever Younger Female. Follow the norms. Read our guidebooks.

Father: We are thinking ahead.

UC 1: As you must. Talk to us. What are you planning for her?

Mother: An excellent culinary school in Switzerland.

UC 2: What? Education? In Switzerland. No, no. NO. Is this what you had in mind?

Father: Of course. What else should we be concerned about?

NNB 1: WIFEDOM. WEDDINGS. RESTRICTIONS. What good will cupcakes—

Grandmother 1: Yoohoo, the uninvited spirits in our living room. It's soap opera time.

Grandmother 2: Today, the surgeon will replace his girlfriend's brain with his ex-wife's.

Grandmother 1: Now fuck off, Dearies. You are bumming out the vibe.

If you ever asked about House CB15A, they would tell you about the strange things that happened inside.

Autoportrait with Windows
Blackwood Crescent
by Tim Tim Cheng

Windows that are thin doors/ you don't step out of/ Windows that catch you with curtains/ like lungs, like mosquitos/ outside/ it tickles / Windows that magpies can't break in/ their blue tails/ the night's hair goal/ Windows that trap pink-feathered, turmeric dusk/ behind your building/ in squares/ blood-orange, blinding/ Windows that deflect/ their phantom gold/ fleeing window sills/ Windows shut/ but a figure is changing/ and you/ shy away/ Windows distilling heat, movements/ into mist/ Windows all green/ Windows beheading/ houseplants gone wild/ Windows telling/ you/ you're not at a party/ Windows with pets/ pets adopting poets/ Windows smokers smoke by/ shoulders leaning towards the street/ Windows you forget/ Windows you don't close/ Windows ajar/ for your dusty heater/ to work/ like a sigh/ Windows where you tell your friends/ overseas/ that you could only sigh/ when neighbours argue/ Windows when they ask/ if you heard/ Windows of saying/ no/ Windows you give/ Windows you don't/ for things/ that touch you/ like love/ like noises/ like the cold/ Windows passing the moon/ skywards/ to each other/ Windows on time-space/ winter, night where you're/ summer, noon/ where friends are/ Windows, a safe space/ Windows/ saying take your time/ Waste it.

Hungry
by Malina Shamsudin

There was once a rotten little boy who was so hungry, he ate an entire house. My house.

Hello. My name is Wich, Eve L. Wich. I'm a pensioner who home-runs a modest confectionary business to busy myself in the twilight years to come. I merge this with a talent for architecture, and a penchant for doing things in extremes. Take my first grand-advertising-cum-abode attempt, for example: A 5,000 square foot cottage built entirely of mouth-watering gingerbread. That's right, entirely edible. Painstakingly garnished with the most decadent of delights: twisty candy canes, berry-jelly filled cronuts, transparent sugar-spun glass, Madagascar vanilla cream icing, Belgian chocolate sprinkles. The works.

It was a balmy Monday morning when I first met *him*. My kitchen was already running like silken syrup: the brioche was baking, the cherry pies were cooling, and the air was filled with the spicy scent of cinnamon. I had just begun whisking egg whites, when I heard it. A distinctive *nibble, nibble*. A distressing *crunch, munch, chomp…smack*!

Single women living alone know the importance of always being prepared. Never known as the cowardly custard of the pack, I armed myself with the sharpest cleaver at hand and proceeded to investigate. Stealthily through the lattice door, around the garden parameter, eyes trained on the roof. What I saw that day still makes my ruby slippers shake.

There was a fat little boy lumped on my roof. Globules of jelly dribbled down his chin. In his hands was pure confectionary carnage. He looked at me then, the sudden move almost dislodging him from his perch.

'You!' I screamed, 'Get down from there.'

'Lent is over lady, I'm taking my dues!' he returned, digging his heels deep.

Transfixed by morbid fascination, I could only watch as the runt's grubby little paws continued to pry chunk after chunk of my signature ruby-rum-gum gingerbread. With a flick of his pink tongue, he seemed to dislocate his jaw to swallow the treats whole. He scootched his bulbous behind across the ridge of the roof, arms outstretched towards the newly installed savoury satellite dish.

That's when it cracked. The roof, I mean.

The sound was like a thunder clap—a sonic shock that pierced my ears. He fell off the roof, landing face down, unmoving, at my feet. Of course, I had to check if he was still breathing. The hefty little lump.

Despite an upper body strength honed by years of stretching dough, I could not make the sticky boy budge. I resorted to kicking him, several times, to turn him over. Finally, like a stodgy pancake, he flipped. His rumpled stained shirt rose up and down, but barely. Now, the child had not been good looking to start with. But since his time on the roof and the descent, his complexion had taken on an unbecoming purplish hue. I screamed for help.

As luck would have it, a fellow neighbour had been meditating by the meadow. Gruff Mr. Wolfe came running. Clocking the unconscious boy, he whipped out his phone to call for emergency assistance. We sat by the boy until help arrived exactly a quarter of an hour later. At least the child was out of the woods. The brioche, however, had burnt.

*

Two days later, I received an exorbitant hospital bill. Liability for negligence.

Two well-dressed suits sat before me, swishing their respective cups of tea. They were seated in my parlour, away from the damaged roof. It was still hard to ignore the protective beeswax tarp that hung overhead.

'The thing is, Ms. Wich,' said Number 1, forgetting the ring of powdered sugar on his gravely pursed lips. 'It's good news that little Hansel Woodkutter III is recovering well in the ICU. Diabetes and minor jaw fracture aside, it seems he was a tad allergic to the gingerbread's secret ingredient—peanut oil.'

'However,' said Number 2, eyeing the last rainbow sprinkle cronut, 'he seems to have contracted mild food poisoning due to the mould on your roofing.'

'Thereby, in accordance with the Mouldy Roof Act 1991 (Section 11A), the authorities of the Ministry of Health and Confectionary Habitat Unit will be quarantining your abode. You are to vacate the premises within 24 hours.'

Number 1 looked back at me. 'Oh, and we're suspending your sugar licence.' He stuck a forefinger into the remaining sprinkles on the plate, closing his eyes as he transferred them into his mouth. 'Perhaps you should have stuck to fibreglass.'

They polished off their tea. And left. Nuts.

*

Neighbours will get you through anything. In addition to the offer of a temporary pull-out couch, Mr. Wolfe stayed by my side. Together, we watched as an enormous tent was thrown over my beautiful gingerbread home. That's 4,000 pounds of caster sugar, 7,400 organic eggs, 7,400 pounds of fine flour, and 2,000 pounds of French butter. A grand total of 40 million calories and so many hours I had lost count. I walked away when the deafening fumigation fans came to life, puffing the tent like pastry.

*

I wish I could tell you that I picked up a spatula and made the most out of the temporary suspension. But my heart was a deflated soufflé. All funds had been channelled towards that dratted hospital bill, leaving little to fix my roof. Without the roof, my home remained 'inhabitable'. My obsession turned online. I trolled through the triumphs of others on the ever popular baking app, Bakergram. I relived my bittersweet glory days, posting pictures of past bakes, including my out-of-bounds gingerbread home, with the tag #foroldtimesbake.

*

One day, I received an in-app notification. Tapping into Bakergram, I clicked onto an icon of a cupcake to open a message. It read: '#BAKEITTILLYOUMAKEIT'. From Gretel_D_gr8.

Intrigued, I scrolled through the user profile: 'Sugar addict. Owner of Gr8 Woodkutter Artist Management'.

Woodkutter? As in Hansel Woodkutter III? The audacity! What more did they want from me? My thumbs hovered over the message bar, prepared to shoot something scathing. Something that would burn and boil. But I drew a blank. Little cookies and cleavers? I backspaced. A skull and crossbones? My phone buzzed, alerting me to a new notification:

Gretel_D_g8: Hi there!

> I see you're in the midst of responding but I
> couldn't wait. Don't be alarmed! This is in no
> way connected to my brother or anyone else.
> I'm so sorry for what you've been through.
> I just love what you do. I know this sounds
> odd…but I'd really like to help you with your
> business. Would you be keen to chat?

She was not what I expected. Where her bratty brother was bold, Gretel was decaf. She reminded me of strawberries in whipped cream–delicate and sweet. But even the best of creams can sour.

We were seated in Mr Wolfe's parlour. Mr Wolfe himself was being discreet, on standby with a cleaver, if required. I placed freshly baked lemon squares on the table. She declined the sweet politely. Tentatively, she sipped her tea. Black, six sugars. I took a seat. I stared at her as I bit into the tart square.

'Ms. Wich, thank you for agreeing to see me. I swear, I was surprised, but so very pleased,' gushed Gretel.

I took another bite of my lemon square, determined to make this as uncomfortable for her as possible.

'The thing is, I think you are so talented, and I would hate for my runt of a brother to have ruined it all. He has a...condition,' she added apologetically.

I stirred my porcelain teacup.

'I want to help you rebrand and relaunch yourself,' she rattled, almost desperately. 'I'm really very good. I am offering my services to you pro bono. Until you see results, of course.'

Instead of shaking a motive out of her, I opted for, 'And how many clients do you have?'

'You would be my very first,' said Gretel. I raised an eyebrow and pushed the treats closer to her. She shook her head, almost regretfully.

'How can I trust someone who clearly doesn't trust me...or my bakes?' I asked.

'Oh, I am so sorry, Ms Wich,' she said, her cream complexion turning. 'I'm vegan. I love sugar, but I can't eat what you have. That's what I had in mind with my rebranding proposal. How about a vegan line?' she said.

Truth be told, I had no expectations on meeting this girl. Nor had I any intentions of saying yes to anything she had up her flowy sleeves. My plan was to somehow crush and annihilate the Woodkutter clan. Using her as bait. That said, Gretel's proposal intrigued me. I had never considered baking without eggs, milk or butter. The term 'vegan' had always assumed a bad taste in my mouth. I could not deny the frisson of excitement at the thought of a challenge. I could make it good.

Plans to annihilate certain members of the Wootkutter clan could be placed on the back burner. 'I'll do it,' I said.

*

Ask any baker worth their salt, and they will say the same: baking is not a matter of luck, it is a precise science. The entire ground floor was converted into a culinary lab. Each surface held potential replacements for conventional baking staples. My vegan experimentation involved a variety of oats, tofu, avocado, and legumes. I set to work, devising creams, gels and foams.

With Mr. Wolfe and Gretel as willing taste testers, I refined my formulas until the end results weren't just palatable, but potentially rivalled the 'real thing' in enjoyment. The next hurdle was ensuring the confection's stability at scale. I started small.

The zucchini tower slid off the table. The rhubarb-and-custard cathedral crashed as well. Attempt after attempt, the structures collapsed. It occurred to me that I did not have to recreate a life-sized vegan gingerbread house. Instead, I opted for going smaller still.

My miniature bakes held better. Sticking to my love for architecture, I handcrafted precise petite replicas of famous buildings. With a magnifying glass, each 1:650 scale model captured the smallest detail. A crack in the Sistine Chapel, visible footsteps on Rapunzel's tower, the gaping hole on a gingerbread house. Each creation was beautiful…and delicious.

As I toiled in the kitchen, Gretel hovered like a hummingbird. She was careful not to get in my way. *Snap, snap, snap, she went. Tippity, tap, tap.* During breaks, Gretel would share tentative stories of a childhood, as if uncertain how the retellings would perform outside her head. Dreams of moving away from her family's lumber business. Her drive to make a boutique talent management agency a success. I began to warm to the girl—the one ripe apple among the rotten bushel.

*

It turned out that Gretel was a marketing maestro after all.

Thanks to her, vegan miniature cakes burst into the Dark Forest scene. Seemingly overnight, everyone was after a taste of the Wich'N Bakes wares. That was my new brand. *Forest* Feed called it 'Bite-sized Bakes You Can't Believe are Vegan'. I had a live demonstration on the popular morning segment, *Miss Muffet's Kitchen*. I even made time for tea with royalty and reality guest appearances on *Grand Architecture Designs* as well as *Extreme Bakeovers*. There is a book deal on the drawing board…'Cooking with Children'.

My success boosted interest in Gretel's boutique talent agency, Gr8 Artist Management. She is now sought after by every rising celebrity in the Dark Forest. Naturally, she still represents me.

What happened to my original Gingerbread House? My pension and modest confectionary business brings in enough for me to consider becoming a multi-mansion owner. Sentimental me preferred to patch up the cottage. As a precaution, I reclassed the property from 'commercial edible' to 'private residence'. This was blessed by the Ministry of Health and Confectionary Habitat Unit. The remodel included a generous test kitchen. Mr. Wolfe stayed on as Chief Quality Control Tester.

What about that rotten little boy that snowballed this all? I saw him at the Farmer's Market once, a carnage of empty sample trays in his wake. The fractured jaw must have required a liquid diet for a while. He looked considerably smaller compared to that fateful night. Loose skin flapped against a bony frame; muscle visibly dry as biscuits that had bled butter under an oven too hot. But his eyes still bore that same inky pit of insatiable hunger. Closer and closer, until he stood salivating before me at my humble stall. My heart missed a beat. My trembling hand held firm to the bold allergen warning. NUT TODAY, MY FRIEND!

It was his mother that saved him from institution interventions, both medical and correctional.

I last saw him being swallowed up by the crowds. The restraining order on anyone with the last name of Woodkutter, save Gretel, still stood. And my stash of EpiPens.

Have I let my success go to my head? Of course not. In fact, if you happen to be in the Dark Forest neighbourhood, stop by my bespoke stall at the weekend market. You can find me personally greeting fans from 10am to 3pm. Oh, and I have diversified my range to include regular bakes—with eggs and dairy! Still in the shapes of miniature buildings. Have you tried the ruby-rum-gum gingerbread? Do read the labels before consuming. You just never know what could change your life.

> FOOD ALLERGY WARNING: Witch'N Bakes products are made from the finest locally sourced ingredients that may contain, or have come in contact with, peanuts, tree nuts, soy, eggs, wheat, shellfish, dairy products, children, bears, spiders, wolves or molluscs. If you have a concern, please contact our customer service representatives at 1-800-BITE-ME.

The excerpt is part of a larger collection of fairy tale retellings set in a contemporary neighbourhood called the Dark Forest.

Gaining Weight
by Amy Curtis

I didn't think getting better would be so hard,
a constant battle between brain and body,
both starving, both screaming
when I pick up a fork;
who knew emptiness could feel so heavy?
I read which fruit shape my figure takes
and another diet endorsed by celebs,
my eyes are attacked by disparaging words,
criticism not just in my head.

Shame sits queasy in my stomach like a sickness,
should I burn or should I binge?
Never full, eyes dull, wearing clothes that don't fit:
looking in the mirror makes me flinch.
Lovers try to give comfort,
trace my stretch marks like a map;
they call me healthy with a smile,
but all I hear is fat.

This body is a burden, I drag it around just for show,
wanting to tear off my flesh like fabric,
strip back down to skin and bone.
Fixating on photos my friends take,
where I'm sucking it all in,
as though owning organs should be a secret;
I only feel pretty when I'm thin.

Peaches
by Olivia Thomakos

Marta raised her eyes to the sky crossed with lightning
and thought of how much she loved spring
storms. She was a climber of fenced
countrysides and an eater of fallen peaches.
Though the thunder was loud, the rain was warm,
pushing air into her windchimes. She listened

to the jingle and hoped the windchimes listened
back. She whistled to them and to the lightning
flashing brightly, illuminating the warm
wooden porch, heated by the day's late-spring
sunshine. Eyes closed, she smelled burning peaches
and crashed through the loose front door. Kitchen fenced

in smoke, she turned off the oven and fenced
against the black billows. The smoke detector silently listened
to her swears, observing the pie of peaches
smoldering in its pan. The windows glowed with lightning
tickling the panels before they decided to spring
from their borders and litter the warm

kitchen with broken glass. Marta's skin was warm
with blood from the shards that had leapt their fenced
frame and dug into her bare legs. She was dressed for spring
turning summer in jean shorts, short sleeves. Wailing wind
       listened
as she whistled, patching herself with Band-Aids. Lightning
bolts watched her clear the pan of peaches

into the garbage. Glass pieces kept the crumble and peaches
company in the trash bag as she pulled on a warm
sweatshirt and taped the window closed against the lightning,
thunder, and rain. A rag and tape fenced
in the smoke detector in case it listened
to the remaining kitchen blackness determined to spring

against the ceiling. Marta often dealt with fires in the spring,
but usually with her neighbors, the ones who grew peaches.
Though she had argued with and listened
to their complaints a hundred times, the night air was warm
with possibility. She was not made to be fenced
in, even when thunder rolled and lightning

shone. She listened to May's last calls of spring.
Led by the lightning, she ran toward the trees of Florida peaches.
Her bare feet warm, crossing a yard that would never be fenced.

Ink of the Evening
by Tamanna Dhuppad

Once Ma and Papa were inside their room, Purab took his place on the sill and peeked outside. It was completely black now and he felt as if he were floating on a boundless ocean. It would be time soon, this day or the next, to tell them that he wanted to pursue dance professionally. There was nothing else he could imagine himself doing. If the evening was anything to go by, he already had his blessings with them. There was only the small matter of making it happen in front of nay-sayers.

Quite suddenly, like pressurised water let loose from a pipe, light from the lamppost flooded the ground. Purab pinched his eyes close to protect them from the onslaught of unexpected brightness. Checking his wristwatch—which showed 11:15—he leaned onto the window, cheek to glass; enjoying its cold on his skin. Nothing else was visible outside except the lamppost like a shining dot.

The air conditioner of the hall had been turned off since the Khaitans left; and the immobility of the air was choking. Purab had almost the mind to pack up and go to his room but the insistent chill of the glass on his face was a sign and this time he slid open the patio door to walk onto the balcony.

Everything was about a thousand times better from here. Better air, better light, better view. All the small homes surrounding his residential building had people safely tucked away in them; and the thought provided comfort to Purab.

A black figure walked towards the lamppost and into Purab's clear view. There were no obstructions to its clear bodily shape, and how it seemed to be…stretching itself, bending on the sides to the left and right. It then faced towards the white houses on the right, and Purab could make out its figure, a curve and a curve, and three-quarters of long gleaming hands protruding from black sleeves. She turned towards Purab's residence and walked towards the shed, which Purab could really only see the top of. She was hidden from his stunned view only for a few seconds before she returned to the same spot, somewhat near the post. Her body loosely waved as she stepped from left to right and vice versa in a rhythm. Purab rushed outside his home with the housekeys jingling in his back denim pocket with thoughts of a pretty pretty face that had caught the light and his attention unwittingly.

*

'Neysa! Neysa, stop! Papa's home, he'll hear you!' Ma barged into Neysa's room, looking for the source that blared music throughout their home, and interrupting Neysa's dance routine. The medium-sized speaker was kept on Neysa's study table and Ma struggled to shut it off, pressing various buttons.

'I've told you time and again to not practice during this time. Why don't you listen to me!?' Ma cried.

Nothing she had done worked because the song was still playing on Neysa's mobile phone, who had kept it hidden from Ma, in the back pocket of her jeans. Despite the increasing sense of frustration, Neysa resisted the urge to turn the volume up.

The next moment, Papa opened the door and walked in, breaking Ma and Neysa out of their panicked conference. His gaze was cemented not upon his wife but his daughter, who staunchly held her own for a few seconds alongside the playing music, before the finger in her pocket and on the phone shut it down with a press. Ma looked from Neysa to Papa in increasing panic.

'Can you tell me your age, Neysa?' Papa asked, very soft in tone.

Neysa chose to not answer, in the anticipation of a harangue and an infant sense of rebellion. Too many times had she been stopped. Too many times, her dance interrupted. How far could he stretch this?

'I have asked you something,' Papa repeated, slow and sharp.

Neysa deliberated switching the music on and resuming her sequence. She knew she was that far gone to bother. That would require space and a sense of peace that could only be obtained once the unwanted left her room.

'Nineteen,' she said.

Papa nodded. 'Nineteen.... A woman already, I'm sure you know.'

Papa's own statements made sure that Neysa's face was devoid of expression. There was no news in knowing that.

She stared on.

'I have always said this for your own benefit. I am tired of repeating it. Again and again and again and yet you persist. Do you not *know* how the men on the street seek to see you? You must know that we live in a small home in a small community and sight travels as fast as words. I am frankly surprised how you do not seem to care for your own security and ours. You *must* know their gazes are trained on your body and this home.'

Excuses, Neysa thought. Pitiful, outdated excuses still clung to. This time she raged, and she wished to scream out her rage so that their ears burst with it. That they'd shudder before stopping her.

'I cannot let that happen under my watch, Neysa. Your security and the security of this house is my responsibility. It was fine when you were a child, but it is disdainful to persist with such vulgarity at your age. Have some care for it and for us.'

In the face of such personal obstruction, Neysa reassured herself. It was her true belief that there were kind people in this world. People that would appreciate her efforts and her talent. People that would love her. Dance was freedom of the body and the mind and the string upon which to hang smiles. All she needed was one more person, with his eyes, his fingers, and his soul full of love. There she would be safe. There *were* people like that in the world, she knew that. So she *was* already safe. It was only a matter of finding them.

Papa took Neysa's silence as his lecture reaching home. He could honestly not bear to hear any more excuses from her. As he uncuffed his sweaty shirt and motioned Ma to set the dinner table, he hoped his softer cadence had made Neysa understand better. It was of paramount importance. He never did understand the youth's obscene passion for dance.

*

Neysa never did go to sleep, when the lights were switched off post-dinner and her parents safely tucked themselves in their room. The fan of her room rotated disgustingly slowly with an annoying creak as a faded beam of white light fell on her body due to the shades being apart.

But that was needed.

She had laid that way for more than an hour, in eager wait for the house to fall completely silent. A very thankful gift, for some reason, that in her humble abode she had been afforded a room with a patio door doubling as a window and opening to a whole veranda, beyond which lay the entirety of gravelled ground.

Neysa got up, making sure to not make a single sound, and collected her phone and speaker. She walked towards the door before stopping for a moment. It had been silent long enough, she considered. Everyone was probably already asleep.

Once outside, the only thing left to do was to scale the thick white wall that bounded the ground. It was easy to hook her arms across the wall and easier to haul her body upwards. To any other person it would have been a difficult task, the wall taller than five feet; but Neysa, with her fit and lean body, scaled it expending only a huff in effort.

For an instant, she worried about having woken any member of her family up, but the spark of fear vanished at the sight of the ten-storey apartment building to her left. She had always wondered about the kind of people that lived in those meticulously crafted homes. The people with their shiny tiles and immaculate walls, and some with their exquisite wooden floors and warmer lodgings. She'd also wonder if a dancer like her existed in homes like these. If they did, they sure must have had it easy, she considered. Men with time and money to spend upondifferent hues of ceramic plates and spoons probably allowed their children to follow their artistic aspirations.

But, nevertheless, this was crucial time afforded to her to resume practice and with all the ground as her stage, that is where she needed to concentrate.

She walked to the shed, climbing its single step towards the frankly terrifying switchboard. She had always hated switches like those: the ones standing blatantly on the streets, and more often than not, coming with that dubious skull and a warning. She pulled down the lever switch with a thud and with a sound as if glass popping, the lamppost began illuminating with gradual increase. There would be a minute or so before it caught its full radiance and Neysa took that time to begin her stretching exercise.

Standing under the light of the post, she bent on the sides to theleft and right. Once done with that one set, she changed her position facing her home. Almost immediately, she faltered with the fear that the lights had woken someone up. But just as quick, she whisked it away and turned towards the high-rise apartments, a view more comfortable than that of her home.

A few more movements, and stretching was done with. She now only needed to set the music and the speakers, and she would be on her way. At the edge of the shed's step, she placed her speaker beside the phone, manoeuvring Bluetooth and song selection.

The bass began thumping. Her body waved as she stepped from left to right and vice versa in a rhythm. As the rhythm resonated more and more with her, she began popping her arms together with it. To the left, to the right, a turn; to the left, to the right, a turn—

—She stopped with abject horror at the sight of a man peeking at her from behind one thin pillar of the shed. His angled stance hardly hid him or his thick arms that his half-sleeves exposed or the fact that he had his eyes cemented on her.

This was bad. This was very, very bad. Fuck this. She'd find another place to dance. She needed to leave.

'Please don't stop!' he cried.

What, did he think that he'd say that and she'd do it?

Neysa sprinted to get her phone and speaker, cursing herself for ever having come here. She hated the unfairness of it all. Was there no place where she could feel safe with her dance?

'Look *please*! I didn't mean to scare you, I swear! I am a dancer too! That's literally the only reason I am here. I saw you dance. The step you were doing—the 'Stick and Roll'—classic Hip Hop! I can show it to you if you want,' the guy pleaded.

For what Neysa considered a foolish moment, she stopped, surprised, and looked at him.

That was enough. Taking that as his cue, he snatched out his phone and scrolled and pressed till Neysa's speaker restarted blue with a blip.

Traitor, Neysa thought at her speaker.

From his space behind the pillar, he walked a few steps towards the light of the post, but not enough to completely illuminate him. He made sure to not walk a single step towards Neysa. Somewhere, he hoped that the increasing space between them would make her comfortable.

He played the most obvious song on the list, Neysa observed. Quite trendy lately. Perhaps something he had danced to, often, and a more comfortable choice than any. He had declared to not simply dance but perform. He took a few moments to stretch in that garish way, not sparing a look to anyone that could see their exhibition, before setting into that same 'Stick and Roll' as he had termed.

He wasn't bad, Neysa acknowledged. His punches were timed well with the twist of his legs. Not an amateur then, she commented to herself. She scanned his figure with a sense of critique, from toe to head, and just when she met his gaze, he pleasantly surprised her by adding more complexity to his dance— a perfect twist of his whole arms to make a circle as he also moved his feet in tandem.

A dancer, then. One who knew his craft. One who came to an empty ground in the middle of the night, amongst sleeping houses, to give a show to no one. Mad enough as her. Any harm that he wanted to do to her, he could've done without taking these pains.

He was a dancer. She was safe.

The excerpt is part of a short story about a boy and a girl bonding over their love for dance and dealing with the social prejudice surrounding it.

Highland Fling
by Heather Dunnett

afair ae wis born ma mither used tae dance
as a bairn ae toddled tae tha tartan trance
out beat beat out touch

ae used tae say 'mither today we learnt this'
an she'd dance it bak fae memory, ne'r miss
back step three four

ae awis wished ae could dance as weel
feet flying cross the fleer, spin fur the reel
out beat beat out touch

ae ne'r did learn tae dance tae her acclaim
but ae felt it singing in mi hirt a the same
back step three four

an ae thocht a ma mither as a quine
an hoo she ne'r forgot in a tha' time
out beat beat out touch

but ae mived awa an dinnae fly nae mair
an mi shoes hung up mak mi hirt sair
back step three four

but hame eence mair, lang syne rung oot
the seed will eence agen dance wi the root
out beat beat out touch

ae siys dance, mither siys babbie aye:
an tae oor bells n pipes, in sync we fly
back step three four

Ye Enly E'r Spik Lik A' Fen Ye're Hamesick
by Heather Dunnett

Ye enly e'r spik like a' fen ye're hamesick.
Ye dinnae de it nae ether time,
Ye spik angelicksied, ye spik English
E'en at hame wi yer een mither ye de.
This isnae how ye spik fen ye spik tae yer fam'ly
Or yer frends or e'en tae yersel.
E'en tae yersel ye dint.
Its a' ye hir fa them, tha chant a theirs,
Ye dinnae, ye dinnae, ye dinnae
It's their wa' a tilling ye tae stop
To cut it oot, to spik mair proper.
Tae spik hoo ye actually spik.

But hoo can ye tell them ye wish tha it wis
Tha ye wish tae spik mair like em tha came afair?
They'd enly e'r laugh a ye
Tell ye it's a damn right joke, to haud yer' dreamin.'
They'd till ye yer nae right tae think lik a'
To spik lik a'
To spik in a tongue that isnae yers
(The tongue disnae fit. They hir it but ye cannae.)

Ye dinnae spik like a' eny ether time,
It's nae fit ye de,
Except for fen ye get like this.
It's nae ye, nae how ye sound, hoo ye are,
Unless ye miss yer hame,
An try to falsely bring it tae ye.

Dialect Glossary

ae	I	haud	hold
afair	before	heid	head
agen	again	hirt	heart
aneuch	enough	hoo	how
awa	away	lang	long
awis	always	mair	more
babbie	baby	mither	mother
bairn	child	nae	no
cannae	cannot	oor	our
dinnae	do not	oot	out
doon	down	roon	round
eence	once	sair	sore
een	own	spik	speak
enly	only	syne	time
fae	from	tae	to
fen	when	thocht	thought
fleer	floor	quine	girl
gin	if	weel	well
hame	home	wid	would

Contributors

SYED AHMED (he/him)
Syed studied English and American literature in the United States and the United Kingdom. There is a classical simplicity and austerity about his stories, a glimpse of a world where, at the heart of poverty and social decay, we witness moments of great human tenderness: intimate encounters between human beings belonging to different worlds. We see surreal Kafkaesque touches and echoes of Cormac McCarthy.

ANNIE BASHAW (she/her)
Annie is a writer from Colorado. Before moving to Scotland, she worked as an engineer by day, writing by moonlight. Though she's switched careers, she hasn't left science behind and loves to write fantasy/sci-fi novels and literary short stories. She has a love for video games, climbing, and cocktails.

BRENDON BEMENT (he/him)
Brendon is a corn-fed Midwesterner from the United States. He graduated from Indiana University, and after four years pursuing a career in film, decided he was better suited for the glamorous and lucrative lifestyle of a writer. He writes silly stories about whatever the heck comes to mind.

JEM BRAITHWAITE (he/him)
A young man with the sad eyes of a horse and the small ears of a pixie.

VENEZIA CASTRO (she/her)
Venezia is a Mexican writer of literary and speculative fiction in English and Spanish. She holds two Bachelor's degrees in

Molecular Biology and Literature, and in 2022 she will complete an MSc in Creative Writing at the University of Edinburgh. Her work has been featured in journals of international reach. You can find her online at veneziacastro.uk.

TIM TIM CHENG (she/her)
Tim Tim is a poet and a teacher from Hong Kong. Her poems are published or forthcoming in *POETRY, The Rialto, Berfrois, Oxford Brookes Poetry Centre, Cordite Poetry Review,* among others. She also translates between Chinese, Cantonese and English. She is working on two chapbooks: one on Hong Kong, another on tattooing. You can find her works on timtimcheng.com.

CHRISTOPHER CORBETT (he/him)
Christopher was a gold medal winner in the men's Alpine skiing at the 2022 Beijing Winter Olympics. He has tied Arnold Schwarzenegger for most victories at Mr. Olympia. He is also the proud owner of The Godfather trilogy on Blu-ray. Most importantly, he's never gonna give you up, never gonna let you down, never gonna run around and desert you.

AMY CURTIS (she/her)
Amy comes from Yorkshire, England, and completed her undergraduate degree at Keele University. She is thinking about pursuing a Ph.D. in poetry on completion of her Master's, so she doesn't have to find a real job. She loves writing about the body and exploring emotion, of which she has a lot, and is most likely still in bed.

ALEX DEDDEH (she/her)
Alex is a Chaldean American fiction writer from San Diego. Her work often features Chaldean characters and culture. Though she hasn't yet mastered meeting deadlines or overcoming her Star Wars obsession, she is grateful to the MSc program for supporting

her through it all.

ELIZABETH DEKOK (she/her)
Elizabeth is a fiction writer from Pennsylvania. After graduating from Susquehanna University, she spent several years working different jobs, hoping that she would find a career that would make her not want to attend graduate school. Fortunately, she failed. When not writing she can often be found haunting bakeries and bookshops. Her work can be found in *RiverCraft*.

TAMANNA DHUPPAD (she/her)
Tamanna belongs to a city called Raipur, located in Chhattisgarh, India. She usually writes fiction in the genres of romance and fantasy and is currently working on her novelette and novella. Apart from writing, you can also find her cosplaying, gushing over K-pop and K-dramas, deciphering Japanese anime and manga, as well as shipping fanfic OTPs.

HEATHER DUNNETT (she/her)
Heather is a queer poet from Aberdeen. She graduated from Edinburgh Napier University in 2021 after writing her dissertation about Winnie the Pooh and Paddington Bear. Her poetry is in both English and Doric (the regional dialect of Aberdeen), and she often writes pop culture works inspired by her love of Disney movies and Doctor Who.

RHIANNON FISHER (she/her)
Rhiannon has been writing mostly long-form fiction since she was in high school. She is from Southern California in the United States and graduated from the University of Redlands in 2019. She has a deep love for mythology, history, and magic, which she often references in her work. She also once accidentally published a "spicy" romance novella on the internet under a relative's maiden name.

VIDISHA GHOSH (she/her)

Vidisha is a novelist from Calcutta. She is passionate about literary fiction, history, *The Master and Margarita*, and hot chocolate. Before moving to Edinburgh, she worked as an independent content writer and editor with different brands and organisations. She loves to write about people, particularly the chaos in relationships and flawed individuals doing the best they can.

AI JIANG (she/her)

Ai is a Chinese-Canadian writer, an immigrant from Fujian, and an active member of the Horror Writers Association. Her work has appeared or is forthcoming in *F&SF*, *The Dark*, *PseudoPod*, *Jellyfish Review*, *Hobart Pulp*, *The Masters Review*, among others. Find her on Twitter (@AiJiang_) and online (http://aijiang.ca).

ERIN KETTERIDGE (she/her)

Erin is a fiction writer from the wide, flat fields of Norfolk, England. She graduated in 2021 from UEA with a degree in Literature with Creative Writing and now lives in Edinburgh. She enjoys people watching, dog spotting, drinking tea, taking long walks on the beach, and being published in anthologies.

ELOISE KIRN (she/her)

Eloise is a lyrical feminist fiction writer from San Francisco, California. She is currently working on a novel, *The Fool*, about a young woman's journey to becoming an artist. Her writing explores themes of female expression, liberation, and the destructive values of patriarchal culture. Her video work has been published by the San Francisco Museum of Modern Art, Business Insider, INSIDER, Vox Media, among others, and has over 800 million views on social media.

HAN LE (she/her)

Han is a poet from Vietnam. She finished her undergraduate

degree in California with multiple writing awards and scholarships. Through her poems, she hopes to remind readers of the presence of positivity and beauty in every experience.

DAPHNE LECOEUR (she/her)
Daphne is a writer from France, fascinated by the concept of empathy, isolation, social deprivation. She strives through her writing to return to the roots of human beings as a species: life, death, love, hate. She graduated from the Sorbonne in Scandinavian Studies, which inspired her to take a more down-to-earth and sensory literary approach.

ANDREW MACKENZIE (he/him)
Andrew is a proudly bisexual writer from Wimborne, England, and graduated from the University of East Anglia in 2020. He writes predominantly works of longer fiction, although he often finds himself straying into other forms, including short prose and screenwriting. Andrew endeavours to write stories and characters that, like himself, do not take themselves too seriously.

GRACE MCDONALD (she/her)
Grace is a student from Lexington, Virginia, who enjoys writing literary fiction and taking spontaneous trips to new places. She graduated from the Virginia Military Institute with honors in 2021 and is currently pursuing an MSc in Creative Writing. Grace also tends to spend all of her money on tarot card decks she doesn't need and Black Medicine chocolate muffins.

EMILY A. MILLER (she/her)
Emily is pursuing an MSc in Creative Writing. Her active imagination was formed from twenty-five years living in a log cabin in Kentucky with much free time, no internet, and forests to explore. She currently resides in Scotland, which affords her many opportunities such as people-watching, Internet, and

concrete to explore.

GIULIA MORICONI (she/her)

Giulia is a writer from Italy and is studying in Edinburgh. Her fiction has appeared in *Tint Journal*, *Cagibi* and *Gingerbread House*.

SARAH NEWTON (she/her)

Sarah is a fiction writer from the swamps of North Carolina who thrives off of coffee, weird cardigans, and bad rom-coms. She considers her greatest accomplishment to be the time she caught a vulture with her bare hands, and you can usually find her ranting about sword fighting and Ancient Greek poets in Black Medicine Coffee over her third mocha of the day.

LINDSAY OSERAN (she/her)

Lindsay is a writer and artist whose stories are often influenced by natural elements from the Pacific Northwest, where she grew up. Her interests include autism self-advocacy and art, and when not writing, she can be found haunting antique shops or forgotten corners of whichever city she inhabits.

TAMARA RAIDT (she/her)

Tamara has been writing poetry in French since she was a child. Now she is writing poetry in English but continues to write fiction in French. She was born in the Swiss mountains. Her childhood spent abroad inspires her to write about belonging, family and the feeling of exile.

SHELBY SCHUMACHER (she/her)

Shelby is a poet and writer from the United States. Having grown up in both the Midwest and the Pacific Northwest, her writing reflects her experiences in both places as well as what it is like to live far from family. A former journalist and photographer, Shelby has covered stories ranging from wildfires to the pandemic. These experiences also influence her writing and how she moves through the world.

ASBAH SHAH (she/her)

Asbah is an aspiring novelist and poet currently based in Edinburgh. Known to be quite uncanny and Victorian-esque in her prose, she usually writes dark fiction with a magical touch. Her work can be best described as a fusion between gothic fantasy, psychological horror, and historical sentiment. A dreamer, a little starry-eyed, and a huge hopeless romantic, Asbah likes to coin herself as an "obsessive book lover, storywriter, and coffee drinker with a slight case of wanderlust." When she isn't roaming Hogwarts or wandering around Wonderland, you can find her stowed away in local coffee houses across the city or singing her heart out during the midnight hours. Being half-British and half-American, she has lived between the United Kingdom and the United States throughout her life, so the word "home" can be quite disorienting to her.

MALINA SHAMSUDIN (she/her)

Malina is a storyteller. Her grown-up stories started in journalism, then public relations for an agency, multinational and non-profit. When not on the hunt for the perfect flat white, the Malaysian can be found grazing on crafty reality TV, talking to dogs, or browsing the children's section of a bookstore.

MEDHA SINGH (she/her)

Medha has authored two books. *Ecdysis* (2017, Poetrywala) and *I Will Bring My Time: Love Letters by S.H. Raza*, a work of translation from French. She has been twice a nominee of the TFA award and edits *Berfrois*. Medha delivered a TEDx talk in 2018. She's currently at the University of Edinburgh.

MADISON SOTOS (she/her)
Madison is a prose writer from Washington D.C. She writes mostly short stories of literary fiction in the realist style. Before coming to the University of Edinburgh to undertake an MSc in Creative Writing, she studied English Literature and Comparative Literature at The University of St. Andrews. Her previously published work can be found in *Lucent Dreaming*.

OLIVIA THOMAKOS (she/her)
Olivia is a teacher and writer from New Philadelphia, Ohio and graduate of the University of Dayton. She is published in *Dreich Magazine*, *Loud Coffee Press*, and *small leaf poetry studio*, among other blogs and university magazines. You can often find Olivia stargazing or sweating through a meal at Mosque Kitchen.

NATHAN S. VIVED (he/him)
Nathan writes long fiction, primarily fantasy. He graduated from the University of California, Santa Barbara, with a Bachelor's in English Literature and Professional Editing. His hobbies include having his head in the clouds, reading, and writing.

BRITNEY WALDROP (she/her)
Britney is a writer from Birmingham, Alabama. She usually writes fragmentary speculative fiction about what it means to be human and the way that the body shapes and transforms the human experience. During her undergraduate at the University of Rochester, she won the Pearl Sperling Evans Prize. She adores used books, the color red, and the beauty of the em dash.

CHANDEEP WIJETUNGE (he/him)
Chandeep is from Galle, Sri Lanka. He isn't sure how he ended up with a background in management, economics, accounting and finance, but give him a good novel, and he's likely to forget all that stuff anyway. Chandeep sometimes takes a break from

trying to write his own novel (about two friends, mostly) to watch football, especially Liverpool F.C.

LIAM WRIGHT (they / them)
Liam is a bisexual, binational, non-binary Creative Writing MSc student from Strasbourg, France, that has lived in Scotland for the past five years. Liam experiments with form, layout and combining multiple speakers and languages in their poems. Their favourite topics include queer experiences, socio-political upheaval, the sea and wildlife, sometimes all in the same poem. They also love lizards.

Lightning Source UK Ltd.
Milton Keynes UK
UKHW010031250522
403462UK00001B/2

9 781739 963521